MOS

EXPRESS

AND OTHER STORIES FROM RUSSIA

MOSCOW EXPRESS

AND OTHER STORIES FROM RUSSIA

GEORGI VINS

LIGHTHOUSE TRAILS PUBLISHING
ROSEBURG, OREGON

2017 Expanded Third Edition by Lighthouse Trails Publishing
2nd printing, 2022
Lighthouse Trails Publishing, Inc.
P.O. Box 307
Roseburg, Oregon 97470
www.lighthousetrails.com

Library of Congress Cataloging-in-Publication Data

Names: Vins, G. P. (Georgi Petrovich), 1928- author.
Title: Moscow express : and other stories from Russia / Georgi Vins.
Description: Expanded Third Edition. | Eureka : Lighthouse Trails
Publishing,
    2017.
Identifiers: LCCN 2017056687 | ISBN 9781942423270 (softbound
: alk. paper)
Subjects: LCSH: Christian biography--Soviet Union. | Persecu-
tion--Soviet
    Union. | Vins, G. P. (Georgi Petrovich), 1928-
Classification: LCC BR1700.3 .V5613 2017 | DDC 272/.90947--
dc23 LC record available at https://lccn.loc.gov/2017056687

For those who are taught by Christ
To subdue the adversities by strength of faith,
The sun of victory will shine
Through the gloomiest clouds.

Georgi Vins, March 1969

CONTENTS

NOTE FROM THE PUBLISHER

Georgi Vins was a young Baptist pastor in the U.S.S.R., when he was arrested for preaching the Gospel. He spent a total of eight years in the prison camps before being exiled to the United States in 1979.

The first part of *Moscow Express* consists of seven stories written by Georgi after he was released and later able to return to Russia after communist Soviet Union was dissolved. These are stories that took place in Russia.

The second part of *Moscow Express* is an extract from the book *Georgi Vins: Testament From Prison* taken from the chapter titled, "My Prison Camp Diary." These were writings by Georgi during his first prison term from 1966 to 1969. The prison writings that made up *Testament From Prison* were smuggled out of the prison and published in 1975 by a U.S. publisher (while Georgi was serving a second prison term—a ten-year term that was later cut in half when he was exiled to America). The legacy of courage and faith that Georgi Vins left behind should never be forgotten.

PART ONE

MOSCOW EXPRESS

AND OTHER STORIES FROM RUSSIA

HOW FIRM A FOUNDATION

How firm a foundation, ye saints of the Lord,

is laid for your faith in His excellent Word!

What more can He say than to you He hath said,

Who unto the Savior for refuge have fled?

The soul that on Jesus hath leaned for repose

I will not, I will not desert to his foes;

that soul, though all hell should endeavor to shake,

I'll never, no never, no never forsake!

(John Rippon, 1787)

ONE

MOSCOW EXPRESS

---◆---

I waited for the Moscow to St. Petersburg express train and observed the bustle about me. I was traveling light, with only an overnight bag and a briefcase, happy to be on my way from Moscow to St. Petersburg to meet with a youth group.

I like to arrive at train stations early. It's fun to watch the flood of life, the commotion of people hurrying on and off the cars like the rushing tides of the sea. Around me swirled an ocean of people, bundles, and suitcases, and in the midst of them, overburdened porters pushing baggage carts like ships cutting through an icy sea as they raise their voices above the din, "Watch out! Careful! Coming through!"

How sweet to hear Russian being spoken again, my native language, music to me since childhood! Nowadays, when I spend the majority of my time in America, just hearing spoken Russian is cause to celebrate.

Slowly, almost noiselessly, passenger trains periodically slid up to the platform. In similar fashion, others glided away without a sound. This is the pulse of the life-blood of Russia in the 1990s. Finally, the "Aurora" arrived, our dramatically named train bound for St. Petersburg. I showed my ticket to the conductor and stepped into the train car. My seat was on the aisle. I set my briefcase on the seat next to me by the window, then I took out my Bible and began to read.

A few minutes before departure, a young woman of about thirty with an expensive leather bag slung over her shoulder entered the car. She stopped in the aisle, looked at me with an impatient frown on her face, and pointed at my briefcase. Though she hadn't said a word, her message was clear. I quickly retrieved my briefcase and stood to let her get to the window seat. Then I sat back down and continued reading. The woman arranged her bag, opened the tray in front of her, took out a newspaper, and became engrossed in her reading. My eyes wandered over to her newspaper, and I saw that it was one of the pornographic publications that had become popular in Russia in recent years. I turned away and continued reading my Bible.

Our train began picking up speed. The Moscow suburbs passed by the window. It was early spring, the beginning of April, and some places still lay enshrouded by snow. After the suburbs came the villages, still naked without leaves on the trees. But winter was already gone, and a feeling of movement toward life, renewal, and freshness filled the air. I pondered other refreshing changes that were taking place across the country.

I had noticed with interest that even major newspapers had begun to write favorably about God. At last, this had become possible! In 1989, I had read with surprise an article in *Literaturnaya gazeta*. In an interview, Academician Amosov, a world-renowned pioneer heart specialist, shared the following thought: "Now we have started to talk about moral values. Let's not mince words. We're really talking about the laws of Moses: Don't steal. Don't kill. Don't lie. An eye for an eye. But the highest ideal comes from Jesus Christ's Sermon on the Mount, and we have a long way to go before we achieve that!" *

Truly nothing is greater than eternal values. To see recognition of the superiority of Christ's teachings in a Soviet newspaper with a circulation of several million readers was incredible! This very newspaper, years before in 1976, had carried a long article titled "Whom Are the American Congressmen Defending," which lambasted me for my faith in God and for preaching the Gospel. (At that time, I was in a prison camp in northern Siberia.) ** Back then the editors wouldn't capitalize the word "God" and used hostile words against Jesus Christ, God, and the Christian faith. Now that very newspaper had printed, "The highest ideal comes from Christ's Sermon on the Mount." I couldn't believe my eyes. How great is our God! He has the power to radically change the very course of history.

---

* *Literaturnaya gazeta*, Moscow, January 4, 1989
** See *The Gospel in Bonds* by Georgi P. Vins

To the measured clickety-clack of the wheels, my neighbor turned page after page of her newspaper. I pitied her and wanted to tell her about Jesus Christ and the value of purity in a person's heart, words, and thoughts. But how to strike up a conversation? Maybe I could politely ask her to put away her newspaper, explaining that I'm a Gospel preacher and it bothered me. But she likely would have replied, "If you don't like it, don't look. It's none of your business what I choose to read!"

I decided to continue reading my Bible without a word. So, that's what I did. This went on for over half an hour. My neighbor kept turning pages as she leafed through her paper. Suddenly, she shut the paper and threw it on the floor under the seat in front of her. She retrieved two books and a notebook from her bag. *Are her books filled with the same contents as that paper?* I wondered. But to my delight, she had an English-Russian dictionary and a textbook for learning English. The woman became deeply engrossed in the English text, pausing frequently to look up words in the dictionary.

We rode in silence for two hours. The passengers next to us were engaged in lively discussions, and I decided to strike up a conversation with the young woman. I turned to her and said in English, "Excuse me. Do you speak English?"

"Very poorly. I started studying not long ago," she said in a manner that indicated she was in the mood to talk.

"Am I interrupting you?"

"No, not at all. In fact, I wanted to talk to you but was a little bashful. Is that a Bible you were reading?"

"Yes, it's a Bible," I affirmed. "I've enjoyed reading it since I was very young. I'm glad that Russia is now open to the Bible. Not long ago people were persecuted because of the Bible. I myself was imprisoned eight years for my faith in God, and now here I am reading the Bible openly on a public train."

"What's your name?" I asked my companion after introducing myself.

"Irma."

"Do you live in Petersburg?"

"No, I'm a Muscovite. I'm going to visit a friend for two or three days. And you?"

"I'm also going to visit friends in St. Petersburg for a few days."

I learned that Irma lived in downtown Moscow, was married, and had an eight-year-old son. She had graduated from Moscow State University and taught Russian language and literature in a high school. Her husband, an engineer, worked in a scientific research institute. They lived with his parents. Her father-in-law was a retired general, and the general and his wife were staunch atheists.

"My husband," said Irma with a smile, "says his parents are dedicated communists stuck in the thirties. They're staunch defenders of the old guard and militant atheism, but my husband and I have a tolerant stance toward religion."

We sat silently for a while.

"Could I see your Bible, please?" Irma asked.

"Yes, of course! Please take a look!"

Irma marked my place and studied the cover and the title page:

THE BIBLE
The Books of the Holy Scriptures
Of the Old and the New Testaments

"This is the first time I've ever held a Bible in my hands," Irma confessed.

Then she opened the Bible where I had been reading. "May I read a bit?"

"Please, go ahead!"

Irma began to read the Sermon on the Mount in Matthew 5 as the train cars rocked back and forth over the rails. It was three o'clock in the afternoon, and we still had a few hours of traveling ahead of us. After a little while, Irma said, "There are some really strong demands made here!" She read aloud: "And if thy right eye offend thee, pluck it out, and cast it from thee: for it is profitable for thee that one of thy members should perish, and not that thy whole body should be cast into hell.'

"How is a person to understand this? And here, about the hand, 'And if thy right hand offend thee, cut it off, and cast it from thee."

"Look at verses 27 and 28," I prompted.

She read them aloud, "Ye have heard that it was said by them of old time, Thou shalt not commit adultery: But I say unto you, That whosoever looketh on a woman to lust after her hath committed adultery with her already in his heart."

"You need to understand, Irma, that the Bible condemns every type of perversion. In the Sermon on the Mount, Jesus Christ specifies that the sin of adultery begins with a look, with a thought, because every action has its origin in our thoughts and intentions. If a person gives free reign for perverted thoughts to fill his heart, then this will eventually lead to immoral actions or, as the Bible puts it, the sin of adultery. Because of this, Christ cautions us to nip in the bud every immoral thought and cast it away before it perverts our actions. Immoral books, pictures, films, and questionable television programs pervert the heart and lead to personal degradation and, ultimately, eternal condemnation."

"Wait a minute," Irma interrupted me. "I think I understand what was starting to happen to me today on the train as I was reading the paper." She blushed. "Umm, did you notice the paper I was reading?"

"I noticed."

Irma turned even redder and hid her face in her hands. She regained her composure with some effort and then continued.

"As I was looking at the paper, my eyes strayed over to your open book, and I realized that it was a Bible. I suddenly felt ashamed of my vulgar newspaper, and I decided right then that I would never again touch those kinds of papers and magazines. Never!"

I listened to Irma's passionate speech, thinking, How great is the power of the Bible! It was just lying open on my tray, and even in its silence, it called this woman to purity of heart. Truly, "the word of God is quick, and powerful, and sharper than any two-edged sword, piercing even to the dividing asunder of soul and spirit, and of the joints and marrow, and is a discerner of the thoughts and intents of the heart" (Hebrews 4:12).

I read to Irma an excerpt from the interview with Academician Amosov and gave her a copy. When our train arrived in St. Petersburg, Irma said to me as she was putting her things away, "How glad I am that we met! You know, I was luckier than anyone else in our train car!"

"Irma," I said, as I turned to bid her farewell, "today is an important day in your life. This is your first encounter with the Word of God. It has lit up your heart and revealed to you the path of life and true happiness in God."

I took a New Testament out of my bag and held it out to Irma: "May this be a lighthouse to your life!"

TWO

GUILTY OF MURDER

---◆---

God, where are You? I'm not afraid of You! Ha, ha, ha! You don't exist! And if You do exist, then kill me for saying so!" a stocky prisoner yelled into the storm. Wearing a dark cap, baggy black pants, soaked jacket and soggy boots, the convict was up to his ankles in mud that had run off a nearby mound of dirt at the work site.

Foreboding clouds loomed above the *taiga.** Cold, autumn drizzle was punctuated by lightning flashes and claps of thunder as the man raised his clenched fists toward heaven and shook them in anger. Rain spattered against his bold and defiant face as he let curses and profanity fly in God's direction. It was a frightening sight: flashes of lightning, gloomy clouds, driving gusts of rain, miserable prisoners soaked to the bone watching Krasnov

---

*A russian term for boreal forest or snow forest.

flailing his fists and cursing. A short way off stood the soldier guards, bundled up in hooded raincoats and snug, waterproof boots. Their huge guard dog nervously pawed at the soggy clay.

At first, the other prisoners chimed in. Even the soldiers urged, "Yell louder, Krasnov! Maybe God can't hear you!" Each successive shout from Krasnov was met with approving laughter.

However, among the criminals, there was one prisoner who was horrified at these curses. Even though Ivan Arkhipov had arrived in the camp only ten days before and was a newcomer in this work brigade, everyone knew he was serving time for his faith in God. When he answered the usual questions on the first day of his arrival, Ivan said he was a Christian who believed in the one true and living God and that he had been sentenced to three years for preaching the Gospel. The other prisoners listened attentively. They hadn't seen this type of prisoner before.

Ivan's work gang was made up of young men mostly eighteen to twenty years old, who were serving short sentences for petty crimes. So Ivan, at 42, quickly earned the nickname "Old Man."

The work gang was supposed to lay a foundation for a railway bed through the swampy taiga. The camp work dispatcher had told Ivan, "I feel sorry for you! I wanted to assign you lighter work like washing dishes in the mess hall or mending clothes in the tailor shop. But the commandant said, 'Ivan Arkhipov goes to construction!

Orders came down all the way from Moscow to use him in the hardest jobs.'"

The first days on construction were especially difficult on Ivan. Up at six, meager breakfast, then work. An armed escort would count the prisoners and march them at a quick pace over rough terrain to the work site eight kilometers away. The prisoners slipped and tripped over old stumps and the rotting trunks of fallen trees.

The railway bed was being laid out on a course that had recently been hacked out of the taiga. Removing the stumps left from the felled Ural pines with their deep and powerful roots was exhausting and backbreaking work. First the prisoners had to dig around the stump, hacking away at the roots to free their grip on the earth, then drag everything to the side of the roadbed. Half of the workday was taken up with simply gouging out the stumps.

The men worked at a fast pace with no breaks until lunch. The cook had a fire going under a big cauldron of stew. The fresh pine forest air mingled with the aroma of outdoor cooking smelled great to the hungry workers. Each prisoner received an aluminum bowl of thick, hot stew and hurried to sit on a log or stump. The hot bowl would burn his callused hands as the prisoner retrieved his personal spoon and ration of black bread from his pocket.

A meal like this can make a man forget he's a prisoner. Perhaps those who haven't experienced real hunger can't appreciate how a half-hour lunch break can become a holiday for a prisoner on hard labor.

Ivan cradled the scalding bowl in his hands, lifted his eyes, and whispered, "Thank You, Father, for this food. Please bless it to my nourishment for Your glory. Amen." He then sat down on a stump, placed the bowl on his knees, pulled his spoon from the top of his boot and a piece of bread from his jacket pocket, and began devouring the meal. After eating, he joined the rest of the men at the brook for a drink of water.

Lunch was over too quickly, and the men had to lug earth and stones and carry them to the embankment of the future railroad. It was hard to keep up the intense pace of the work. But the team leader kept pushing, "Faster, faster, come on!" His two prisoner assistants did no work themselves, but walked around with sticks, shouting orders, "Come on, come on! Get a move on!" In addition, they would prod anyone who wasn't hustling with the rest.

Ivan tried with all his might, but prison life was indeed taking its toll on him. His hands would get so tired by the end of the day that he could hardly grip the shovel. Ivan tried to keep up so the others on his team wouldn't suffer the consequences if his share of the work lagged. *Lord! Help me*! he would call out silently. Quitting time was five o'clock, but it was still a two-hour hike back to the camp.

On his third day, Ivan witnessed a ghastly sight. A young prisoner who couldn't keep up fell under the weight of the load. A taskmaster ran up to him with a stick in hand and, cursing, started striking him as he struggled back to his feet. At lunch break, the miserable young prisoner went off a short distance, put his left hand on a stump, and chopped off his fingers with an axe. Then he raised the bloody hand with two fingers still dangling, hefted the bloody axe with the other hand, and bellowed, "It's better to die than do this slave labor!"

Everybody froze, staring at him. The young man planted his foot on the tree stump and raised his axe for another blow. "Halt!" the team leader yelled savagely and snatched the axe from his hands. Two guards ran up and grabbed him, but he tore himself away with a loud yell. The soldiers immediately ordered the work gang back to camp. They bandaged the mangled hand in a rag, but the blood just kept flowing. A prisoner on each side propped him up and helped him walk, but shortly he was spent. The guards ordered his work mates to carry him.

Ivan overheard the team leader ask, "Why did you do this? You'll get even more time for chopping off your fingers!"

"I can't go on!" the agonizing man replied. "I don't have the strength. I've wanted to hang myself for a long time now but could never bring myself to do it."

"Don't say a word about getting hit by a supervisor today," the team leader warned.

"Of course not! Why would the brass need to know about it?"

———◆———

Now, on Ivan's tenth day in the prison camp, the downpour continued, making it the second time that he and his work gang had to spend hours out in the rain. But today the most unbearable thing for Ivan was not even being drenched to the bone but rather the almost inhuman howling of curses toward God. "What makes this guy scream like that?" Ivan asked a prisoner next to him as he wiped the rain off his face with the sleeve of his jacket.

"That's his soul crying out. He murdered the old woman who lived next door to him, ended up here, and now he screams," the other answered.

In the end, everybody got sick of this ongoing farce, even the soldiers. The team leader yelled, "Krasnov! That's enough! Shut your trap! Get over here with the rest of the crew!"

The prisoners grumbled, "Come on, quit it! You've howled and yelled and gotten it all out of your system, so that's the end of it." But Krasnov continued to blaspheme and shriek.

"Hey Krasnov, stop your wailing, or I'll loose the dog on you!" one of the soldiers ordered.

That worked. Victor Krasnov shut up and clambered down from the embankment. Soon afterward, the escort led the prisoners back to the camp. They trudged along as quickly as possible, with each step pulling their feet out of the wet clay. The curses still rang in Ivan's ears. To clear his mind, he kept repeating to himself, "The fool hath said in his heart, There is no God. They are corrupt, they have done abominable works, there is none that doeth good" (Psalm 14:1).

After this incident, Ivan began looking for an opportunity to talk to Victor Krasnov. But Victor was sullen and reclusive.

One Sunday afternoon, everyone noisily tramped off to watch a film in the mess hall. Ivan stayed behind in the barracks, pulled out his notebook of Bible verses, and began reading and adding other verses from memory.

Suddenly, aware that he wasn't alone, Ivan looked around and spotted Victor on a lower bunk by the door. So he went over. Victor, with his sullen expression, looked up and said, "Hey, Old Man. I hurt inside. I don't feel like living anymore!"

"What do you mean by that, Victor? You've already served half your term. Just a little while longer, you'll be free," Ivan tried to cheer him up.

"What good is freedom? It's even worse than this!" Victor answered dejectedly.

Ivan went back to his bunk and retrieved the notebook from under his mattress.

"Would you like me to read you something from the Bible? I've got it copied down here."

"Here it goes about this God again! The Bible again!" Victor sprang from his bunk in a rage. "Didn't you hear how I mocked your God on the embankment? He didn't even bother to strike me with a bolt of lightning! It means He doesn't exist! Quit your preaching! The officials were right to imprison you. They were too easy on you. People like you should be shot!"

Ivan went back to his bunk, knelt, and began to pray. Suddenly, something struck him in the back. Ivan looked and saw an old boot lying on the floor. Victor laughed. "Get my message? Now don't come crawling to me with this God of yours!"

Soon, the barracks was bustling with noise again as prisoners returned, engaged in lively discussions about the film. Victor suddenly yelled, "Who let this Baptist in here? He was just now trying to convert me! And he's keeping a notebook with stuff from the Bible under his mattress!"

Everybody fell silent. Ivan's bunkmate whispered to him, "Quick! Give me your notebook. I'll hide it. They're gonna do a search now."

Ivan passed the notebook to his neighbor. A work leader, a broad-shouldered man of about thirty, walked up to Victor. "Is that you bleating again, Krasnov? This is a prison camp, not a community meeting. You murderer, you don't even have the right to cross your eyes!"

An hour later, an officer and two soldiers made their way to Ivan's bunk. The officer frisked him while the soldiers searched the mattress.

"Where's the Bible?" asked the officer.

"In my heart," Ivan answered calmly.

"You just keep up that talk! I'll send you off to isolation!" the officer threatened before he and the soldiers exited the barracks.

———◆———

About two weeks later, the work crew was building a wooden bridge over a small creek. The main tools for the job were the usual axes, shovels, and the prisoners' bare hands. This time, they also gave the prisoners a power saw for sawing down the largest pines. The process of tree-removal was simplified: one man sawed through the trunk about a foot and a half above ground level while another would use a pole to push the tree until it toppled. The man pushing had a dangerous job with much responsibility, for no man alive had the strength to control a tree if it began to fall in the wrong direction.

That's exactly what happened once, when, under the force of a strong wind, the top of a tree began leaning the wrong direction. The man pushing shouted, "Look out!" and slid out of the way himself. The man operating the saw also managed to move, but others didn't notice that a tree was hurtling down in their direction. Hearing the yell, everyone jumped out of the way—everyone except Victor Krasnov. Ivan swooped down and tackled Victor, both of them tumbling to the ground just as the mighty pine crashed, pulverizing smaller trees and bushes. It landed precisely where Victor had just been standing.

Ivan noticed that Victor was pale and so shaken that he couldn't even speak. His first words were, "Thank you, Old Man. Forgive me what I said before. It was your God who saved me just now!"

From that moment on, Victor stopped cursing God. As he spent more time with Ivan, he stopped using foul language altogether. Little by little Victor told about his past, his family, and the fateful day of the crime that landed him in prison. He also shared his fears. Eventually, the full story unfolded—a mixed-up, bloody mess that held no good promises for the future.

Victor had been sentenced to eight years' imprisonment for the murder of an elderly woman. All the details of the crime had been so well thought out in advance that many years went by before anybody even saw Victor's hand in the affair. As a result, an innocent neighbor was tried for the murder and sentenced to fifteen years. Not until eight years later was it discovered that Victor was guilty. (The neighbor was immediately released with his prison record wiped clean and two months' salary from his last place of employment as compensation.)

At Victor's trial, this man was called in as witness. He ranted and demanded the death sentence for Victor. He even demanded a trial for the judge who had wrongfully sentenced him. The judge stopped him, saying, "Witness Petrov, calm down! We know that you suffered innocently, but today's hearings are unaffected by the fact that you were erroneously sentenced in the past. You have the right to request that your judges be brought up on charges, but everything must be done according to the legal processes. Submit a petition to the high court, and they'll call into account those who allowed this error in your case."

But Petrov kept on screaming in the courtroom, "For you, this is just some kind of 'error,' but I lost eight years of my life in prison camp! My life is ruined! My wife abandoned me and filed for divorce! I'm a stranger to my own children! Who's going to fix all that for me? At my trial eight years ago, I tried to prove that I didn't kill her, but they sentenced me anyway. I sent complaints and notices to the high court requesting that they reconsider my case, but all I got back were the same form letters saying that I had been tried justly and that I had no grounds for appeal."

Again, the magistrate tried to silence Petrov, but he cried out the more as he pointed to Victor, sitting on the defendant's bench, "Execute this fiend! If the court spares his life, I'll carry out justice myself! I'll hack him down with an axe, just as he did to old Maria!" A great commotion erupted in the courtroom. Victor's heart sank, and he dropped his head. Everyone had turned against him.

"Silence!" The judge vainly tried to pacify the witness. "That's enough! With threats like that, you'll talk yourself right into another eight years!"

Petrov was undaunted. "Remember. Victor, if they don't let you hang, I'll do the job myself!"

At which the judge raised his voice. "Petrov, no threats! Only the court will decide what punishment to measure out. This is the court's duty, not yours!"

Victor listened with growing fear. He understood clearly that two different punishments lay ahead: in this court, he would be sentenced to a term, and then, if he survived, there would be a meeting with Petrov. Victor related all of this to Ivan.

"Well, did you really kill Maria?" Ivan asked.

"Yes, I killed her, even though I didn't want to," Victor said sorrowfully. "My mother-in-law set all this up. She had me do the dirty work, but she was so clever that no one even thought of me as a suspect. The suspicion fell on Petrov, Maria's neighbor. A week before the murder, he got into a heated argument with her, after which he went outside in a drunken stupor and began threatening her, 'I'll hang you out to dry! I'll kill you with my own two hands, you hag!' Many neighbors overheard the threats, and Petrov was arrested immediately after the murder. But eight years later, they arrested me when my mother-in-law gave me away. I admitted to my part during the investigation."

Victor returned to this topic over and over again in their evening talks.

"You know, Ivan, to this day, I can't figure out why I agreed to kill her. Maria and my mother-in-law used to be such great friends. Maria was even my wife's godmother. When I married Dunya, Maria loved me too, and then loved our baby daughter. Maria really helped our young family. As a widow with no children, she lived alone, and if we ran out of something, she'd share with us."

"But, Victor, how could you agree to kill someone?" Ivan asked. "Maria was like a mother to you and your wife. You could have said no to your mother-in-law, and that would have been the end of it."

"But that's just it," Victor responded sullenly. "I was afraid of her. I was a young country boy, and she was a very controlling woman. About two years after Dunya and I married, she wanted us to divorce because I wasn't earning enough money. On top of that, she knew one of my secrets: my friends and I used to steal boards, paint, and nails from building sites. We sold it all on the side for money to go out drinking. So, she had me in the palm of her hand. She threatened to turn me in to the police. She would say, 'I'm going to go down and turn you in. Then they'll throw you in prison, and my Dunya will find someone better!'"

"So how does Maria fit into all this?" Ivan was struggling to understand.

"Who knows? How did good friends become enemies? Probably money. Maria had been stashing away for years, and maybe my mother-in-law wanted to get at it."

Victor also told Ivan about his childhood, about his parents, and about how he wound up in the city. He was a middle child with three brothers and two sisters on a remote collective farm in the country. Life was hard during those years in the country, especially since their father was killed during World War II.

"There were few men around during the war," Victor recalled. "I began to work on the collective farm as a small boy, tending cows and sheep. They paid very little for our work. We lived off what we planted on our own plot and kept some chickens and a cow. But we also stole everything from hay for the cow to grain for the chickens. My brothers and I, like all the other guys around, swiped whatever we could from the fields."

Victor's mother was a God-fearing woman in her own way and used to pray in front of the icon hanging on the wall in her bedroom. She'd often tell her children, "Stealing is bad. It's a sin. Never take from people what's not yours. But taking from the collective farm isn't really stealing, since everything there belongs to all of us. What can we do if they hardly pay us for our work? Are we to die of hunger?"

Ivan listened, trying to figure out how a country lad ended up committing a beastly murder.

When he was seventeen, Victor fled the collective farm and went to the city, where he got a construction job and lived in a dormitory. This new city life was hard for him, since he had no friends or relatives, and the dorm was a den of drunkenness, brawling, and thievery. A year later, Victor met a young lady at the construction site who was three years his senior, and he married her. He had always dreamed of having a happy life, and he loved his Dunya, but they lived with her mother, who turned out to be a domineering woman.

Two years after Victor's wedding, his mother-in-law planned the murder. Victor knocked at Maria's door by night.

"Who's there?" Maria called from behind the door in a sleepy voice.

"It's Victor. Open up!"

"Why are you coming in the middle of the night?" she marveled as she opened the door.

"They sent me to fetch some potatoes," Victor answered. He reeked of vodka.

"Hey, aren't you a little tipsy?" Maria eyed him attentively.

"We had a party, and my mother-in-law drinks like a fish. Then she gives me too much to drink." Victor sat down at the small table in the kitchen. In his hands, he held an empty bag. "They push me out of the house in the middle of the night to go after potatoes, and if I don't go, then I get yelled at till dawn."

"Yes, she really makes it tough on you. She's upset with me about something too, though I can't figure out what. How many potatoes do you need?"

"Oh, a bucket full."

"I'll get them for you right away. Take off your coat and stay awhile. Why are you sitting there all bundled up?"

"I'm in a hurry, Maria. I've got to be at work in town in the morning." Victor's eyes scouted around the room for the old woman's axe. There it was—next to the firewood by the wood stove.

Maria opened the trap door to the cellar and went down with the bucket. She gathered up the potatoes and began climbing the stairs. Just then, Victor struck her in the head with the axe. Maria fell into the cellar before she could even utter a scream. Following his mother-in-law's instructions, Victor didn't take off his mittens as he closed the door to the cellar, grabbed his empty bag, and turned off all the lights in the house. Then he peered outside. It was the dead of night. All was still, and not a soul was stirring at two o'clock in the morning. *This has worked out great!* Victor thought, but a heavy weight hung about his heart. *It's nothing. It'll pass with time*, he comforted himself as he wandered off into the night.

A week later, the neighbors became concerned. "Why haven't we seen Maria? Surely, something must have happened to her." They notified the police, who immediately found that the door was unlocked, the house was cold, and the bed was not made. Then they opened the door to the cellar.

A forensic specialist determined that the murder had taken place about a week earlier and that the murder weapon was an axe found at the crime scene. Other than the scattered potatoes and the empty bucket, the police found no further evidence. The victim's belongings were all intact. Therefore, the investigation determined that the motive for the crime was probably revenge. The neighbors remembered the drunken threats of her neighbor Petrov, and he was arrested.

As Victor related the details of the murder, a cold chill ran down Ivan's spine, and he became nauseated. *What horror, what a heinous act!* he thought. *How could someone take the life of another human being and then go on living as if nothing had happened—listening to music, eating, breathing, and playing with his child?*

In the prisons and camps, Ivan overheard many tales of violence, murder, and other monstrous crimes. Prisoners often bragged of their crimes, portraying themselves as brave and decisive while their victims had somehow earned their unfortunate fate. They even implied that those victims were somehow at fault for *their* imprisonment, saying cynically, "It's because of people like that that we made a name for ourselves in prison!" Rarely did Ivan find someone among them who was sincerely sorry for causing sorrow to others.

Ivan pondered a great deal about this hardness of heart. Where were its sources? He came to the conclusion that its roots were atheism: the rejection of God as the Creator and Judge of every man's action and thought. Again, he was reminded of the words of the psalmist:

"The fool hath said in his heart, There is no God," and as a result, people "are corrupt, they have done abominable works, there is none that doeth good" (Psalm 14:1). Everything he was seeing at the camp confirmed for Ivan how accurately the Bible describes the condition of mankind, "The whole world lieth in wickedness" (1 John 5:19).

Watching the prisoners and observing what brought them satisfaction created in Ivan deep distress for people who had been reared in atheism and, as a consequence, were now so hardened. "If an enemy doesn't surrender, then he must be eliminated!" they taught everyone from the first grade onward. So, a generation had grown up in which the masses were cultivated with a sense of hate and hard-heartedness. That same kind of teaching had created the likes of Victor's mother-in-law, Victor himself, and millions of others like them. "What miserable people! Poor Russia! Lord, save our people! Send freedom to preach the Gospel because only the light of the Gospel can save Russia!" Ivan prayed as he lay on his bunk.

As time passed, Victor began to spend all his free evenings with Ivan. They spoke of many things. As Victor tried to ease his conscience, he often turned conversations to the topic of his crime, still blaming his mother-in-law. One time, Ivan asked him, "Victor, how is it that, after the murder, you were able to live peacefully for eight years while another man was being punished for your crime? How could you possibly allow that?"

Victor was silent, but Ivan continued. "Victor, not a single human deed will go unrewarded. Even though Maria is dead, there is a God, the Supreme Judge, who sees all and knows all. You will receive inner peace only if you repent before Him, the Judge of your conscience!"

Without saying a word, Victor got up and left the barracks. From then on, he began to avoid Ivan. He even requested a transfer to another work brigade and was sent to live in a different barracks. When Victor bumped into Ivan in the camp, he would turn the other way. But Ivan continued praying for Victor.

In the barracks and during the short breaks to catch their breath at work in the taiga, Ivan testified to the other prisoners about God. In a short period of time, a small group of men were seriously interested in faith in God. They met to discuss what was read from the Scriptures. (One of the guards secretly brought a New Testament into the camp.) The camp administration was alarmed at Ivan's spiritual labor and unexpectedly shipped him away to another camp.

———◆———

During Ivan's physical exam at the new camp, the doctor determined that Ivan had a hernia.

"What kind of work did you do in the previous camp?" the doctor asked.

"I worked on a construction gang."

"Well, then it's understandable why you've developed a hernia. You need an operation, and for the time being strenuous work is out." The doctor summarized his final remarks in Ivan's file.

Ivan was sent to work as an electrician in the electrical division. The machinery building stood next to the living quarters, and the crew leader was a calm, serious man of about forty. He immediately began asking, "Are you an electrician? Do you know motors?"

"Yes, I know motors," Ivan answered.

"How about automotive electrical wiring?"

"No, I never had the chance to learn any of that."

"No problem. You'll pick it up quickly." The man smiled. "So what are you in for?"

"I believe in God. I'm a Christian," answered Ivan.

"Now, that's interesting! I knew a believer in my last camp. He was a good man. Straightforward. Honest. Since you're a believer, that means you'll work honestly. People like that are hard to find. What camp were you in before this, and what jobs did they put you on?"

Ivan named the last camp that he'd been in and briefly told about the work building the railway in the taiga.

The crew leader became thoughtful. "Well, here the conditions will be easier. We're not going to have you moving heavy objects around. You'll do your time on electrical work. Actually, I won't be work leader around here for long. There's only a little over three months left before my release. My term is only two years. Child's play!" The man laughed. "This is my second term. The first time, I served eight years for someone else's crime. For 'an error of the court' they told me afterward. That's when I lived in Tambov."

"What's your name?" Ivan quickly asked.

"Vasily Petrov. What's with that look on your face? Have we met somewhere before?"

"No, we haven't met. Your story sounds familiar," Ivan answered, wondering: *Is this the same Petrov that Victor talked about, that neighbor of Maria? Look how this turned out!*

The lunch bell sounded, and the work brigade was taken to the mess hall. After lunch, the work leader came over to Ivan again. "I myself haven't been in this camp very long—just over a year. Before here, I was in a camp in Siberia. There was a Christian in that camp, probably one of yours. He told me a lot about God and was always trying to talk me into forgiving the guy who had done me wrong and had caused me to be imprisoned the first time."

"What was this Christian's name?" Ivan asked.

"Nikolai Petrovich. He's an old man."

"Khrapov?"

Petrov nodded. "You actually know the guy?"

"I know him well! He's my brother in the faith and my good friend," Ivan exclaimed.

Back at work, Ivan thought a lot about their conversation, almost certain that this brigade leader was the very man of whom Victor had spoken. That evening in the barracks, he decided to ask.

"Listen, Petrov. You said they tried you in Tambov. Weren't you Maria's neighbor?"

At this, Petrov's eyes grew wide in surprise. "How in the world did you know that?"

"I was in prison camp with Victor Krasnov, and he told me about his case."

"That's impossible. You served with Vic? Where is he now?"

"We served in my last camp together."

"Listen, Ivan, let's go out into the yard to talk for a minute!"

They put on jackets, left the barracks, and walked around the compound for a long time, talking right up to lights out at ten o'clock. Petrov said that he began to drink heavily, carouse, and brawl after Victor was sentenced. Several times, he was hauled in to the police, but each time they let him go because they remembered that he had already served eight years for a crime he didn't commit. But Petrov continued in his petty crimes. One time when he was walking downtown, he happened to see the judge who had sentenced him to the fifteen years he didn't deserve. He began to harass her right there in front of people and even struck her in the face several times. Some passersby came to the aid of the woman and grabbed hold of Petrov, but he continued screaming at her, "I'll kill you! Give me back my eight years! Give me back my family!"

At this point, a police car pulled up, and Petrov landed in jail, this time with a felony offense. At the trial two months later, to everyone's surprise, the battered victim asked that Petrov be pardoned.

"He's suffered a huge tragedy," she said. "I once made a serious error in handing down a sentence in court, and this man was the victim of that error. I know that he has committed a felony by attacking me, but I ask the court to reduce his sentence to a year."

The judge, considering the defendant's request, sentenced Petrov to two years' incarceration (not the three to eight years prescribed by the criminal code).

The next evening Petrov continued his tale. "My second term is coming to a close, and the best thing about those years was meeting your friend, Nikolai Khrapov. My talks with him turned my life around. I was in despair and turned against everyone. Then I met this man who had spent the greater portion of his life innocently behind bars, solely for his faith in God. But his spirit didn't waver, and he didn't become embittered.

"Nikolai Khrapov told me a lot about God all those months we were together. During one of our talks, he said, 'Petrov, stop serving the Devil! Think about your soul. You need Christ! Repent before God and begin to serve Him!' When he was being released, he pressed my hand and didn't let go for a long time. 'Petrov,' he said, 'I believe some day you will become a Christian! Believe, repent before the Lord, and He will accept you as His son. Now promise me that you won't take revenge on Krasnov.'

"'Don't rush me,' I said. 'I'll think about God.' But I did promise him not to take revenge against Victor Krasnov and not to hold a grudge."

Ivan and Petrov walked for a long time along the snow-covered path between the wooden barracks as dusk was deepening. The windows were covered with frost, through which shone a faint and melancholy light. The whole camp had the atmosphere of a forbidden zone, with high-powered beams from the guard towers' search-lights scanning the yard and bright glints from flashlights tracing the wire around the six-meter-high outer fence.

There, on the guard towers, soldiers dressed in warm greatcoats, fur hats pulled low, and warm boots stood watch around the clock with machine guns ready. After dark, they would take turns firing rounds into the frozen, winter sky. The night air was gripped by the bitter cold, and the snow crunched underfoot as Ivan and Petrov walked. Over the taiga and the camp hung the infinite heavens, where scattered stars twinkled like living orbs of light.

Ivan removed his hat, raised his face to the heavens, and began praying out loud. "Our Father which art in heaven, Hallowed be thy name. Thy kingdom come. Thy will be done in earth, as it is in heaven. Give us this day our daily bread. And forgive us our debts, as we forgive our debtors. And lead us not into temptation, but deliver us from evil: For thine is the kingdom, and the power, and the glory, for ever. Amen."

Following Ivan's example, Petrov also removed his hat, at which the cold instantly bit into his ears and face. But he paid no heed as he quietly repeated after Ivan the words of the Lord's Prayer.

———◆———

Thirty years passed. The camps in the Urals became a distant memory for both Ivan and Petrov. In the 1990s, the Lord brought an amazing time of freedom for preaching the Gospel in Russia. Ivan, advanced in years and gray by this time, continued witnessing to his people about Christ. After a worship service in Siberia, a tall, old man approached him and asked, "Do you recognize me?"

Ivan studied his face intently. Something was familiar about it: he had seen that face before . . . But where? When? Suddenly the other smiled, and Ivan was overtaken with joy. "Vasily Petrov!"

"The very same! Greetings, Ivan, my brother in the faith and in my chains." They embraced warmly.

The two spent the rest of the day together. "I've been following the Lord now for thirty years. Oh, what happiness! The memories from my former life without God are like a nightmare!" Petrov shared with his old friend the story of his fate after they had parted company in the camp.

As it turned out, Petrov didn't go back to his hometown after being released but instead moved to Siberia, where he began attending a Baptist church. A year later he repented and was baptized. His family was restored: his wife and children agreed to join him in Siberia. It wasn't long before his wife became a believer, and the children soon followed.

"What about Victor Krasnov? Do you know anything about him?" asked Ivan.

"I searched for him a long time. I wanted to witness to him about Christ. Then, about ten years ago, I happened to get Victor's address from a man I knew back home. Victor had moved to a small city on the Volga. I took a vacation, and my wife and I went to visit him."

"But didn't you think the sight of you might scare him off, considering your former threats?" asked Ivan.

"Yes, I did have that concern," Petrov confided. "When the address finally led us to Victor's apartment, his wife Dunya greeted us. At first, she didn't recognize me. She asked who I was and why I had come. Victor wasn't home because he was laid up in the hospital. I reassured her that I hadn't come for revenge. I was now a Christian and had the best of intentions. Dunya cried, 'My Victor is on the verge of death, and lately he's been asking me to bring him a Bible. Victor remembered a man who had spoken to him in prison about God, but Victor shunned him. Now he's sorry that he didn't listen to that man, and there's no way to undo the past. I took a Bible to the hospital for him, and he reads it all the time.'"

Petrov and Dunya went to the hospital together. In that room were two beds: on one, a sick man was sleeping, and, on the other, a pale, emaciated man looked at Petrov with anxiety. Dunya brought a stool, and Petrov sat down next to the bed.

"Hello, Victor! I've come to visit you."

"Hello." Victor weakly held the outstretched hand. "How did you find out where I live?"

"From Sergei Zastolniy. I've been looking for you a long time, all these years! But don't be alarmed, I've come to you only for good. I'm a believer, and I want to tell you about Jesus Christ."

"Look at me now. I'm not long for this world! I heard a lot about God from a Christian named Ivan while I was in prison. But I had it in for the whole world then. Here in the hospital, everything that Ivan said at one time or another has come back to my mind. I asked Dunya to bring me a Bible, and I'm reading it little by little."

Victor was choking as he gasped for breath. Dunya put a second pillow under his head. Breathing heavily, he asked with anxiety, "Can you forgive me?"

Petrov pressed Victor's hand. "I forgave you long ago! The Lord Jesus taught us to pray, 'Forgive us our debts, as we forgive our debtors.' I forgave you, but you need to ask God's forgiveness for murdering Maria and for all your other sins. Do you realize that you are a sinner?"

"Yes, I'm a horrible sinner! Not only did I kill Maria, but I also caused grief to many others."

"Have you asked God to forgive you?"

"No, I haven't."

"Do you want God's forgiveness?"

"Very much!"

"Then let's pray."

Petrov knelt by the bed, and Victor, holding his hand, began to pray with tears in his eyes. "Lord, forgive me, a horrible sinner!" Dunya stood next to him, tears streaming down her face. Petrov also prayed, thanking God for His unspeakable love toward men.

Petrov continued telling Ivan the story. "My wife and I spent several days in their city. I visited Victor every day in the hospital. He didn't want me to leave his side. Victor died in my arms, ready to meet the Lord. Before his death, Victor said, 'How happy I am that you've forgiven me. But I'm even happier that the Lord has forgiven me. I was a fool to reject Him so long, but now I'm going to meet Him, just like that criminal that Christ forgave on the Cross!"

With that, Victor stepped into eternity.

"Where is Victor now? Where has he gone?" Dunya was troubled over the next days as she grieved her husband's death.

"To the Heavenly Father's eternal mansions of light!" Petrov consoled her. He read to her and her daughter verses from the Gospel of John, "For God so loved the world, that he gave his only begotten Son, that whosoever believeth in him should not perish, but have everlasting life. For God sent not his Son into the world to condemn the world; but that the world through him might be saved. He that believeth on him is not condemned: but he that believeth not is condemned already, because he hath not believed in the name of the only begotten Son of God" (John 3:16-18).

So, several decades after their first memorable encounter in the prison camp, Ivan rejoiced to hear about God's work of grace in the life of Victor Krasnov.

Georgi Vins with his wife, Nadia, and their two children Natasha and Peter in 1958, a few years before his first arrest.

THREE

YOUR JOB IS
ON THE LINE!

———◆———

In the autumn of 1962, the *Evening Kiev* newspaper featured an article hostile toward Christians. It attacked Baptists for their faith in God and the active life of the church in what was supposed to be an atheistic society. The author was particularly annoyed that church ministers happened to be highly educated professionals. The paper included my wife and me in the list, even citing the place where I was employed as an engineer and the high school where my wife taught English.

The article agitated, "How is it that the Soviet government has given these people higher education, and yet they believe in some sort of god? In addition, they are engaged in religious propaganda, infecting children and youth. How can we let them work in Soviet schools and responsible positions in the city of Kiev? What does the management do about this? How can they put up with these people in the workplace?"

The Communist Party expected this publication to bolster their ideological stand against religion, but the opposite happened: the article created in Kiev's two million inhabitants a great interest in the Baptists and their faith.

The day after the article appeared, it became the subject of discussion in every department of the engineering firm where I worked. I overheard some of my co-workers' comments, "Just think about it: we thought that believers were old-fashioned people with little education—backward old men and grannies in the villages! But it turns out they're educated people, young professionals who believe in God and preach the Bible. And so many Baptists! What a surprise! So maybe faith in God isn't just gloom and doom! That's interesting . . ."

Some were negative, "All these Baptists should be sent to Siberia, to the farthest reaches of the North! The fiftieth anniversary of Soviet power is coming up, and Baptists have no place in our society!"

News at work tended to spread quickly, "That guy will be fired."

"This guy's in line for a promotion."

"So-and-so left his wife and kids to live with such-and-such woman."

All such "advance reports" were eventually backed up either by a pink slip, a promotion, or by the fact of divorce, whichever the case may be. The disseminator of this "news" was usually a certain Zaporozhets, an engineer in the electrical division. He was tall, with brown hair, about thirty, energetic, sociable, and extremely helpful. "Excuse me, could you please allow me to take just a moment of your time? I've just heard the most dreadful thing, and I wanted you to be the first to know. By the way, I haven't seen you around for a couple of days. How are things? How's your health? Say, have you heard yet about?" Such was the verbal stream that Zaporozhets was constantly pouring out for the nearest listener.

The engineering firm where I worked was located in a four-story building in Pechersk, a lovely neighborhood of Kiev. About 400 staff, consisting of engineers and technicians with various areas of expertise, worked there. Zaporozhets was the most unique and well-known personality at the firm. Everyone knew him, some loved him, the rest at least tolerated him. Zaporozhets never harbored ill intentions; he was congenial and kind-hearted, but a non-stop talker. He spent most of his workday not at his drafting table, but in action. For example, if some item needed to be procured for the management, bureau director Nikolai Nikolaevich would call Zaporozhets into his office and give him the responsibility of tracking it down.

Zaporozhets was part of the electricians' department, which I supervised. He would often say, "Georgi, I won't be in today or tomorrow. Nikolai Nikolaevich is sending me on an errand! But don't worry, my blueprints will be finished by the deadline, and they'll be great!"

So, he would disappear for two or three days. When he showed up again, his time, as usual, would be spent running from floor to floor, department to department. He always had some news to share. True to his word, his drafts were always done well and on time—he worked quickly and with concentration, and stayed overtime if necessary. We had a good, friendly relationship, and this became strikingly clear when things started to get tough for me at work.

The morning after the *Evening Kiev* article appeared, I got to work and found that stony silence reigned in the electricians' room as each person worked at his desk. No one even looked up when I walked in. I decided to beat them to the punch, "It sure is quiet in here today! Did you all read the article?"

Everyone burst to life at once. "We read it!" their voices resounded.

"I don't believe our newspapers. Everything's always blown out of proportion in them! Whenever a newspaper starts campaigning, they always write in sweeping generalities, just to push people's buttons. Now they're pushing an anti-religious cause, and that's just how they write." The first person voicing an opinion was a senior engineer of about 35, who was quiet and good-natured at work, constantly concerned about her children. Her husband had died a few years before, so she was rearing two school-age children on her own.

One of the technicians, Misha Pugachev, strode up to me and took me by the arm. "Georgi, don't worry! Everybody here respects you, including Nikolai Nikolaevich."

"What's so bad about religion?" someone else noted. 'Don't steal.' 'Don't kill.' Nothing wrong with that!

Besides, according to the Constitution, we have freedom of religion."

At this moment, Zaporozhets flew into the room and declared, "Georgi, the whole institute's buzzing like a beehive! Almost everybody's behind you. Let's step into the hall for a few minutes."

Zaporozhets pulled me to the window at the end of the corridor, where we were in absolute privacy. "Listen, we're all outraged at this spiteful article!" he said excitedly. "Only Kostov from the construction division is against you. When I ran by there this morning, he was yelling to everybody in the room, 'This Baptist needs to be kicked out of here and put on trial! He should have his parental rights stripped and his children taken away!' But I took the wind out of his sails."

Right then, into the corridor stepped Yefim Shtulberg, lead engineer of the construction division as well as deputy Communist Party secretary. Shtulberg headed in our direction. "Excuse me for interrupting. Georgi, come with me. We need to discuss an electrical wiring job for the factory."

I accompanied him to the construction division. As Shtulberg opened the door to a large room containing over thirty desks, we heard many voices mingling in animated discussion. All conversations abruptly stopped when they saw us. Everybody got back to work, and only Kostov, standing at his desk, looked at me with a mocking smile. For about twenty minutes, we studied blueprints and the wiring design. As I was walking out the door, I nearly stumbled over Zaporozhets going in. As the door closed behind me, I heard voices shouting on the other side.

Later, I found out what had happened. No sooner had I left than Kostov turned to the head of the department and said, "Why do you allow that Baptist to come into our department?"

To which the other answered, "I invited him in myself on business concerning electrical wiring."

"But didn't you read the paper?" Kostov retorted. "This Baptist has no place at our facility! We need to call an institute-wide meeting, fire that guy, bring him to trial, and take his kids away!"

An eruption of murmurings broke out in the room. Getting in Kostov's face, Zaporozhets yelled, "You're the one who needs to be put on trial! You abandoned your family, your own kids; yet you go around sporting the rank of a Soviet engineer! You're the one who needs to be kicked out of our facility for moral aberration!"

The grumbling got louder. Just then the director's secretary poked her head through the door and announced, "Nikolai Nikolaevich says for everyone to get to work and stop wasting time on the clock!" She walked through the whole building, quieting everyone down. Zaporozhets came back into our room and silently set to work.

The next day, Zaporozhets said to me, "The director and the party secretary were called to Party headquarters this morning because of that article!"

I barely knew the director of the institute, having met him only two or three times. But I knew Party Secretary Vladimir Kryukov very well. He was also an electrical engineer by trade, ten years my senior, and had fought on the front lines in World War II. He had been a Communist Party member since the beginning of the war. He had lost a leg on the front and now walked with a prosthetic and a cane. We had worked together on several projects, and he visited me at home two or three times when my wife and I lived downtown. Ours was a cordial relationship.

Three days after the article came out, I was summoned to Party Secretary Kryukov's office. He, deputy director Shtulberg, and Kurakin, another official, were waiting for me. Kryukov spread the newspaper out on the table, its pages open to the article. Several lines had been underlined in red. Shtulberg asked me, "What do you have to say about this?"

"What should I say?" I shrugged. "I believe in God, and I won't deny it. You all knew I was a Christian before this was printed."

"We knew something or other about you being a Christian," Kurakin replied, "but that on off hours you were a religious propagandist—that's something we just found out. Now that this article has appeared in the press, this whole Baptist business is making us all look bad!"

"This is serious, Georgi," Kryukov added. "Yesterday, the director and I were summoned to Party headquarters downtown. They wanted you fired immediately. They told us that a criminal case has been started against you and that they intend to strip you of your parental rights. Your children will go to an orphanage—I pity them. Think about your children! As the Party secretary and a war veteran, I used my influence to spare you from strict measures. I promised that we'd straighten you out. They laughed at this idea at Party headquarters, but then agreed to it, 'Give it a try! If you're successful, then we'll award you the Golden Star of the Hero.'"

Kurakin chimed in, "Georgi, come on and do it so he can get the Golden Star!"

Shtulberg interrupted. "Enough joking around! Georgi, tell us about your faith and how you came to believe. What plans do you have for the future? You can be open with us. We're not enemies. We want to understand you and get a handle on this unpleasant situation."

So, I told them how I believe that God, the Creator, made the earth, the sun, the moon, the plant and animal kingdoms, and us, human beings. I told them how, at age sixteen, I realized I was a sinner, and that only Jesus Christ, who had died for my sins on the Cross, could give me salvation and eternal life. I was baptized in the summer of 1945 when, in the presence of many believers, I gave my promise to God that I would live for Him. My wife has also been a believer since she was fifteen. We have three children, I told them—Natasha, 9, Peter, 6, and Lisa, our baby. As a Christian family, we don't hide our faith from the children. We read the Bible with them, pray, and attend worship services together. This is the most important thing in our lives.

"How are things going for your wife where she works?" Kurakin asked. "The article says she teaches English in the upper grades."

"Yesterday, there was a faculty meeting at the school. They demanded that my wife deny her faith in God or else lose her position."

"How did she answer them?"

"She said that believing in God gave meaning to her life. She was fired."

"Georgi, has it ever occurred to you that you and your wife are some sort of backward fanatics?" asked Shtulberg. "Think about it: you graduated from Kiev Polytechnic Institute, and your wife graduated from Kiev University. Even after that, you're still both believers? And you even teach your children to believe in God? On weekdays, you're a lead engineer, and on the weekends, you're a Baptist preacher—how can you do both? Please explain!"

The interview continued in this vein for about two hours. I never found out their official decision on this matter. When I was asked to leave the office, I ran into Zaporozhets, who had been pressed up against the door listening. He abruptly turned and took off, telling everyone his version of what had occurred: "Four men went into the Party secretary's office: one Baptist and three communists. Two hours later, out came three Baptists and one still deciding!" Of course, he was exaggerating, but I knew that God had given me the opportunity to tell the bosses about my saving faith in Him.

The next Sunday, about 150 Christians gathered for worship in the forest outside of Kiev. Suddenly, KGB workers and police fell upon us as we were on our knees praying at the end of the service. They tried to arrest the preachers, but a large group of young people encircled us. After an hour of physical struggle, the police left for reinforcements. We all headed home.

When we got off the commuter train back in town, we were met by more KGB and police. They fell upon us again, intending to arrest the preachers. We huddled, then broke into singing a Christian hymn and all set off together down the street. The KGB began to beat the believers and ended up arresting nineteen of us. We were locked up in Lukyanov prison. A day later, fourteen people were released, but five of us were given fifteen-day terms. My personal acquaintance with Soviet prisons had started. I was 32.

When I returned to work fifteen days later, I discovered that, by order of the director, I had been demoted from supervisor to the engineering pool. Two months later, the director finally called me into his office.

"I defended you earlier before the Communist Party officials, but now the matter has gotten out of hand. It's either you or me. If I don't fire you, they're going to remove me from my position as director. It would be better if you simply resign."

"All right, I'll give notice," I agreed.

———◆———

All this happened in 1962. Over thirty years later in 1995, I visited a congregation of Messianic Jews in Kiev, where I had been invited to preach. Over one hundred Jews who had received Christ as their Messiah and personal Savior attended. I was touched to hear them sing the Psalms of David in Hebrew.

At the end of the service, during a question-and-answer time, an older man about my age then stepped up to the microphone. He looked up and said, "My dear Georgi Petrovich, you've probably already forgotten your co-worker Isaiah [and he gave his last name] from the engineering bureau. No wonder, it was over thirty years ago! Yet I remember you well because I followed your story for many years. I read everything they wrote about you in the newspapers, but I didn't believe the press. I just want you to know that I'm a Christian now! God lives in my heart. I believe that Christ is the Messiah of Israel and my personal Savior. So now, I'm your brother in Christ!"

After the service, Isaiah came up to me, and we embraced. I don't know what became of my other co-workers, nor of those three bosses who summoned me in 1962, but I've prayed many times for their salvation as I reflected on the past. May the Lord grant that some day before God's throne we may say, "Four men went into the Party Secretary's office in June 1962—three Communists and one Baptist. But after a few decades, four Christians met in eternity at the feet of Jesus!"

FOUR

OVERNIGHT TRAIN

———◆———

The express train eased away from the platform in Odessa. It was the summer of 1995, and my daughter, Natasha, and I were returning to Kiev. The conductor brought our linens, and Natasha made our beds and lay down to rest. Our three days in Odessa had been hectic. I decided to read a little. Sharing our compartment were two men who greeted us, stowed their baggage, and went out to the corridor. I had the impression that they were traveling together.

An hour or so passed, and one of them came back with his linens and prepared his bunk. He slipped off his shoes, and as he peeled away his socks, I saw that his legs were covered with tattoos of stars and chains. I had seen this sort of thing before on thieves and other hardened criminals in the prison camps. *Looks like trouble!* I thought. How will this night turn out? This young man slid easily up to the top bunk and was soon fast asleep.

A little while later, the fourth passenger entered our compartment. He began to spread sheets on his bunk, and I noticed tattoos on his arms. *I wonder if he has tattoos on his legs, too,* I thought, but he climbed up on the bunk with his socks still on. Soon, he was asleep. The train rolled on through the dark night as its cars rocked gently over the tracks, lulling us to sleep. I prayed, committing our trip and us into God's hands, thinking of David's words, "I will both lay me down in peace, and sleep: for thou, LORD, only makest me dwell in safety" (Psalm 4:8). This verse had often been a support for me especially during the time I served in the prison camps.

When I awoke, it was already light. I left the compartment to wash up. Our companion with the tattoos on his legs followed me into the corridor. After washing up, I knew I wouldn't be able to fall back to sleep, so I decided to read. Our neighbor soon returned, hopped back up to his bunk, and also began to read. His book looked familiar, very much like a Bible. Lying on the bunk with his head against the window, he was reading intently.

"Excuse me, may I ask you a question?" I said to him.

"Yes, of course!" The man turned his face in my direction.

"That wouldn't by any chance happen to be a Bible you've got there, would it?"

"Yes, I'm reading the Bible!"

"Are you a Christian?"

"Yes. Are you?"

"Yes, I'm a believer, too."

At this point, I remembered his tattoos and decided to confirm my hunch. "Were you ever in prison?"

My neighbor laughed. "You're a very observant man! Yes, I served my time as a thief. But that's all in the past now. Last night I noticed you checking out my legs with the tattoos. I bet you didn't sleep a wink all night, tossing and turning?"

"Actually, I slept very well; the Lord is my shield. I myself served eight years for my faith in God, and when I saw your tattoos, I immediately knew where they were from. That was why I was so surprised to see a Bible in your hands. By the way, what's your name?"

"Sergei, and yours?"

"Georgi Petrovich. Sergei, how did you come to faith in God?"

"I was born and grew up in Odessa," Sergei related. "When I was five years old, my father left my mother with three children. Mama raised us by herself. But she was always at work, so mostly I grew up on the street. Boyish mischief led me into committing my first crimes, and by the time I was fifteen, I ended up in juvenile detention. My second term was in an adult prison camp. I got out, got drunk again, stole something, and got a third prison term, this time in Lvov. I used drugs, drank, and smoked, and by the time I was twenty-five, I was so sick and tired of that kind of life that I started looking for something pure and bright."

The other guy jumped down from his bunk and began to put his shoes on. Sergei suggested we step into the corridor. We stood by the window as he continued his story. "A group of Christians began to visit our camp every Sunday afternoon. They sang, read the Bible, and answered questions. Some of my buddies started going to these meetings. One of them gave me a New Testament to read, and these words caught my attention, 'Blessed are the pure in heart: for they shall see God.' I began to think a lot about God, about faith, and about clean living.

"I read through the Gospel of Matthew and decided to attend the meetings. When my buddies sang along with the believers 'Jesus, Savior of My Soul,' I saw in their eyes hope for a new life. Their lives had dramatically changed for the better. Before long, I also believed on Jesus Christ and got a new, clean heart.

"I wrote two letters: one to my mother and the other to the girlfriend waiting for me in Odessa. I told them about the changes in my life and my happiness in God. I asked their forgiveness for having caused them so much grief. In reply, I received two difficult letters. Mama wrote, 'I'm sick of your endless schemes and adventures! Why can't you just live like normal people? Now you're on a faith kick. This is just a crazy new scheme for you! Stop fooling around, finish your sentence, and come home—only without God!'

"My girlfriend wrote, 'I fell in love with a daring, maybe even risky guy, but you've gone off your rocker, and now you're reading psalms. Sorry, but I don't need you if you're going to be like this!'

"Two years ago, I was released and went home. Mama was a bit leery at first, but when she saw me get a job and noticed that I didn't drink or mess around anymore, she rejoiced. In Odessa, I found a church and was baptized. I play the guitar and sing. Before I became a believer, I loved to sing dirty songs, but now I play Christian songs.

"I made new friends, young believers who often visited my place in the evenings, and we would sing together. Mama really liked my new friends. My girlfriend started attending services, repented, and gave her life to the Lord. We've been married a year now, and not long ago our son was born. That's the short version of my life. Sometimes I come across old friends and witness to them about the Lord."

"Sergei, what does your mother think about all this now?"

"She started going to church and has some Christian friends."

"Where are you headed now?"

"To attend a week-long seminar in Kiev for young preachers and learn a few things. I took a week off from work so I could go."

I looked at Sergei and thanked God. How amazing are Your ways, O Lord! How good and merciful You are to each of us, giving us salvation and eternal life!

"What about the other passenger?" I asked. "Is he an acquaintance of yours? His arms are also tattooed."

"No, I don't know him. We just got tickets right before the train's departure and ended up in the same car."

About an hour remained before we were to arrive in Kiev, so we went back to the compartment and gathered up our bedding. Sergei stowed the mattresses from the lower bunks overhead. I introduced him to Natasha, "This is Sergei from Odessa. He's going to Kiev for a seminar on evangelism."

"I was saved only three years ago from a life of crime," Sergei added. "I was convicted three times. But now, praise God, everything has changed: I got saved in prison. By the time I left, over twenty other inmates had become Christians. The administration even gave us a room for Bible studies."

I noticed the other passenger watching Sergei and listening to every word. I decided to tell my story.

"I was also imprisoned twice, not for any crime, but for my faith in God. I served a total of eight years in the northern Urals and Yakutia. I was released the last time in 1979. When I was in prison, we were not allowed to have a Bible. However, I had a tiny copy of the Gospel of Mark that I let others read, but it had to be kept hidden. I have been a believer since I was 16 years old, and now I'm 67—that makes half a century that I've been following Christ."

Sergei interjected, "In my last camp in Lvov, two of my buddies put their faith in God, and then I did. We began to witness to our fellow inmates and the administration. We even wrote to our old friends in other camps, telling how our lives had changed and urging them to turn to God."

The other guy spoke up. "Say, that wouldn't happen to be your letter that got circulated through the prison camps about two years ago, urging people to give up the criminal life and turn to God? I was a prisoner then. Oh, excuse me for not introducing myself. My name is Yaroslav."

All three of us—Sergei, Natasha, and I—stared at him in astonishment.

"No," Sergei answered, "that letter was from my friend Vasily. His faith was really strong. His old buddies beat him up a few times because he had become a Christian. But he was no coward and simply said to them, 'Just wait. Soon the Lord will be knocking at your hearts, too.' And sure enough, a few of the same guys who roughed him up ended up coming to the faith."

The train pulled into the Kiev station. I said in parting, "What interesting traveling companions ended up in one compartment: three former convicts! Maybe our whole car was filled with ex-cons?"

We all laughed. Yaroslav said, "Probably everyone in our whole country has some connection to prisons: one served time himself, another had relatives or acquaintances who served time. That's just the kind of country we live in with those kinds of laws!"

Sergei disagreed. "I don't know about the rest, but I deserved what I got. I committed a crime, and that wasn't the fault of the laws."

"I suppose you're right," Yaroslav agreed. "It wasn't my faith in God that got me locked up, either."

I pulled two copies of *The Gospel in Bonds* out of my bag. "I wrote this book," I explained, "to show how faith in God was put to the test in the prisons and concentration camps. I want to give you each a copy to remind you of our meeting on the train."

They each thanked me. As he grasped my hand in a farewell handshake, Sergei said, "I have an exciting week ahead of me, meeting new friends, seminars on the Bible! The Lord is already blessing this trip, even on the train starting early this morning!"

I bid a hearty farewell to Sergei, this former criminal and now my brother in Christ. I shook Yaroslav's hand and urged him to seek God. Yaroslav thanked us for the interesting conversation and asked, "Do you and your daughter need a ride? Friends are coming to pick me up, and we can take you wherever you need to go."

"Thank you, Yaroslav, but someone is meeting us."

Natasha and I went out to the square in front of the station and waited for our ride. About ten minutes later a sleek, black Mercedes pulled up. Next to the driver sat a smiling Yaroslav. "Hop in," he said. "We'll be happy to take you!"

"Thanks, Yaroslav, but if we're not here when our friend shows up, he'll get worried."

"All right. All the best to you, then."

"All the best to you, Yaroslav! I'll be praying for you!"

The Mercedes zoomed off to the city.

"Who do you think that fellow is? Mafia, maybe?" Natasha asked.

"Hard to say. Maybe a businessman, maybe Mafia. However, one thing is beyond doubt: he has an eternal soul and needs God!"

A few minutes later, Vladimir Kofrun, a local pastor, pulled up in his twenty-year-old Moskvich. His little brown car had been patched up time and again but was still serving him all around Kiev in his itinerant ministry to small churches as far away as Chernobyl.

As I got into the car, I smiled at Natasha, "Here is the Mercedes that's come for us!" Vladimir looked at us inquisitively. As we rode home, I told him about the two men on the train. One had found God in a prison camp and now personally testified of God's love. The other had just today heard of the way of salvation in Christ. Move his heart, O Lord!

A GROUP OF IMPRISONED JEWS AT AUSCHWITZ CONCENTRATION CAMP—MAY 1944

FIVE

NO GREATER LOVE

When I was traveling in Ukraine during the spring of 1995, I met in Kiev Andrei Bassarab, a friend of my youth whom I had not seen for several decades. He told me the following story of a Jewish Christian, a courageous Gospel preacher during the Second World War.

On August 22, 1941, the German army occupied Cherkassy, Ukraine. Two months later, Jews all over the city were arrested, including children and the elderly. The rounding up of Jews began downtown and spread to the outlying regions. David Zaveryukha, a Gospel preacher and a Jew by nationality, lived with his family in a duplex shared with another Christian family.

Early one morning toward the end of October, a German army truck stopped outside David's home. An officer climbed out of the cab while armed soldiers jumped out of the back and surrounded the house. The officer and two soldiers entered the house, and about fifteen minutes later David, his wife, and their three children stepped outside carrying small bundles.

The Christian neighbor saw what was happening and ran outside. The soldiers began threatening him with their rifles and did not allow him to approach the family in custody. David managed to call out, "Goodbye, brother! Until we meet before the Lord!" A soldier yelled at him and began to buffet him into the truck with the butt of his rifle. "Schnell! Faster!" Jews were being taken to an old prison in Cherkassy, which is where they took David and his family.

The following day, Christians gathered at the pastor's home to discuss what had happened. They prayed and set about deciding what to do. Someone suggested, "We need to go to the German commandant and ask for David's family."

But he was countered, "The commandant is a hot-tempered man. He has already been approached on the matter of the Jews who have been arrested, and he yelled at the petitioners and threatened to throw them in prison as he kicked them out of his office."

"Looks like all we can do is pray," one of the men said.

Another opened his Bible to Proverbs 24 and read, "'Deliver them that are drawn unto death.' That is what the Bible teaches. We should pray and act! My suggestion is to petition the German commandant and go see him."

Another spoke up. "Remember the words of our Lord, 'Greater love hath no man than this, that a man lay down his life for his friends.' As for myself, I am willing to go see the commandant."

It was time to end their meeting since a curfew had been imposed from dusk until six in the morning, and no one dared violate the curfew. The men prayed and departed, resolved that the next day three of them would go to the commandant with a petition in hand.

The following morning, they met again to compose the document. After signing it, they committed everything in prayer into the Lord's hands. The German military headquarters was situated downtown on Lenin Street, guarded by armed soldiers. At first, they didn't want to let the men through, but the Christians wouldn't leave. Finally, a petty officer took charge of them with an interpreter in tow.

The interpreter began reading the petition to the officer, translating from Russian to German as he went. When the interpreter finished, the officer crumpled up the document and threw it on the floor, yelling, "You came to ask about a Jew? Nothing will come of it! No one will release him from prison! Get out of here!"

"Sir," they implored, "please allow us to speak personally to the commandant!"

The officer started yelling again and ordered them out of headquarters. They picked their petition off the floor and went home, resolved to try again.

The next day, they returned to headquarters, requesting to speak to the commandant, but they were again expelled. The scenario repeated itself this way for two weeks: each day they went to headquarters, and each day they were kicked out and threatened with arrest. All this time, the church was praying for God to intervene in the fate of David's family.

Finally, after two weeks, the commandant agreed to see them. Through the interpreter, he listened to their petition, in which the believers had written that David Zaveryukha was a Christian, that he had preached the Gospel for over twenty years in Baptist churches, that he was an honest worker and an exemplary family man, and that all of them had known him for many years. The letter concluded with the request that David and his family be released and placed under the responsibility of the local Baptist church. Several dozen believers from the city of Cherkassy had signed the document.

At first, the commandant spoke to them very curtly. "What do you need this Jew for? You've been clamoring for him for two weeks now, but that won't help him. Don't come here anymore!"

"He is our brother in the faith, and we will not leave him stranded!" they answered.

"Jews are arrested on orders from Berlin. I'm carrying out my orders!" the irritated commandant replied.

But the Baptists didn't leave. "Do a good deed. Release our brother David Zaveryukha with his family."

The Lord softened the heart of the commandant, and he called his assistant into the office. "Prepare an order for the warden of the prison to release this man with his family. He poses no threat to the German government. Once you have the document ready, I'll sign it, and then you will give it to these people."

The Christians thanked the commandant and left his office. An assistant instructed them to return for the document two days later. They fervently gave thanks to the Lord for this manifest mercy. On the appointed day, they received the document indicating that David Zaveryukha and his family were to be released from prison right away. They took it straight to the warden of the prison, where gaining admission was not an easy task. But again, the Lord helped them.

The prison warden read through the order and called a soldier in and said something to him in German. The soldier motioned to the Baptists with his hand, indicating that they should follow him. He led them to the gates of the prison where they were to wait. About thirty minutes passed. At last, the gates opened, and they saw David, his wife, and their three children in the prison yard. David said something to his wife, then crossed the yard and passed through the open gates to where his friends stood. He hugged each of them.

"Thank you, brothers, for your intercession for my family! I want to tell you what's going on in this prison. On my first day here, I began preaching about the crucified Christ to the Jews incarcerated here. In these difficult circumstances, awaiting death, many of my kinsmen gladly listen to the Word of God. In these two weeks, about twenty people have turned to the Lord and received Jesus Christ as their personal Savior. I believe God Himself sent me here so that I may testify of His name. And if now I forsake my Jewish brothers that are condemned to death while I am set free with my family, then they might turn from Jesus Christ and from all that I have preached to them. Then I would be guilty before the Lord. When my wife and I heard just now that we were to be set free, we decided to stay here and accept our fate with all the rest of the Jews."

David spoke calmly and confidently. "My brothers, I hope you will understand that I want what the apostle Paul wanted, 'that I might by all means save some.' I'm here to help those who have turned to the Lord in prison to become firm in the faith. May they also meet death with steadfast confidence and hope that they will be with Christ for eternity!"

David turned to look at his wife, and she was nodding full agreement. The men cried. David hugged each of them, saying, "Until we meet in heaven!" Then David prayed and returned to his wife and children who were waiting in the prison yard. The gates slowly closed. With heavy hearts, all the men went home and reported to the church. Together they knelt in prayer, asking the Heavenly Father to strengthen David and his family for the fiery trial awaiting them. None of them ever saw David or his family again.

———◆———

In November of 1996, I requested a fuller account of the 1941 mass annihilation of the Jews in Cherkassy. Rabbi Boris Kaplan of the synagogue in Cherkassy supplied the following information:

"The German army rolled into Cherkassy on August 22, 1941. In October, the German commandant was given two orders concerning the twenty thousand Jews living in Cherkassy. In one, it was written that all Jews were required to register with the municipal police. In the other, they were required to abandon their homes and move to the Jewish ghetto in Mytnitsy.

"In November, the Germans eliminated the first group of Jews, 1500 people whom they shot in a park by the railway. The remains of 18,000 more people executed by the Germans, most of whom were Jewish, are interred in three common graves near the village of Belozerye."

. . . giving thanks unto the Father . . .

who hath delivered us from the power of

darkness, and hath translated us into the

kingdom of his dear Son: in whom we have

redemption through his blood, even the

forgiveness of sins. (Colossians 1:12-14)

SIX

TALK OF THE TOWN

———◆———

Everyone in the town of Zarechny was talking about Kostya Zabolotny, a thief and a drunkard. Something big had happened to Kostya and suddenly he had stopped pick-pocketing, robbing, and drinking. They said he had even stopped smoking. According to one of the grannies sitting outside on their benches gossiping on summer nights, Kostya had been transformed into a "God-fearing man." Somehow, these elderly women were always the first to find out the latest news. Now everyone was talking about it, just about the time Kostya finished serving his latest prison term and came back home as a Christian.

Everybody in town knew Kostya since he was born and raised there. As a small boy, Kostya started stealing chickens and geese from the neighbors. Later, he stole wallets from passengers on trams and buses. "I take whatever people have hanging around, and, as a rule, I only steal from half-wits," Kostya gloated in front of his friends. "Don't drop your guard, buddy. Watch your pockets. I'll keep the money, but, of course, I'll mail back all important documents to the owner— that's my rule. I keep my work classy and refined!"

Kostya was a teenager when he lifted the fateful purse that first landed him in juvenile detention. A few years later, he was released, but he quickly got arrested again. So his life sped along in this bitter rut: winter, summer, prison, a little bit of freedom, then arrest and back to prison again. As an adult, Kostya started expanding his trade across the wide expanse of Russia. But he was a hometown boy, and every time he got released, he made a point of first going back home to Zarechny.

Kostya's parents had died long ago, and a distant relative lived in their dilapidated old house. Whenever Kostya was home, he'd work on house repairs, mending the roof or fixing the old fence and gates. Kostya swept through like a mending whirlwind, and his drinking buddies helped out, laughing and banging hammers all day and then partying at night with vodka, cards, singing, and dancing. The neighbors used to join in the fun; even some of the old women would show up for a drink. Kostya catered to all, and all were happy. Sometimes fights would erupt during the bashes, but Kostya would break them up.

Kostya was strong and powerfully built, with big hands, a muscular neck, and broad shoulders. His deep-set eyes flashed from beneath thick, dark brows. His voice was deep. Whenever one of his buddies crossed the line of "decent drunken behavior," Kostya would walk up to him, grab him, and lift him off the floor with just one word in his deep, booming voice: "Enough!" The perpetrator usually sobered up and just muttered, "All right, you big bear. Let me go! Hey, guys, Kostya's mad."

But everything changed when Kostya turned 35. He was in a Siberian camp where a few thousand inmates were serving their sentences. Some twenty Christians were in the camp for their faith, and in their time off work they would get together. Among them was Nikolai Khrapov, a Christian poet and preacher. Kostya met him and liked talking with him. The things that Nikolai said sounded new and unusual, and Kostya began to read the New Testament and joined the small meetings of Christians. Before long, he got saved and stopped drinking and smoking. He told his old prison buddies about the change in his life, then abruptly stopped hanging around with them.

One night, the thieving "guild" planned to hold a forum in one of the barracks. As far as they were concerned, Kostya had compromised the "code of thieves," which might cost him his life. They summoned Kostya, who immediately went to consult with Nikolai Khrapov. They quickly prayed together, and Kostya went to the meeting as summoned where he found ten of the chief thieves gathered in a circle. One of them drew his knife and threw it to the floor in the middle of the ring as an open threat. The meeting had taken on a serious nature.

"Is it true that you've left the racket?" the owner of the knife asked. "And do you know what happens to men who leave?" He pointed to the knife.

"I do," Kostya replied.

"Who talked you into leaving? The warden?" another asked.

"You all know good and well that I never snitch to the brass, and I'm not hooked up with them now. I've left my former life because I became a Christian. Now I believe in Jesus Christ."

"Come on, tell us what happened to you, and what's next," ordered the boss.

"My conscience bugged me for a long time, and I decided that stealing and bloodshed wasn't the way for me. Before I didn't know what to call it, but now I know it's sin. The Devil had me in his clutches. The Bible says plainly that thieves and drunks won't inherit the Kingdom of God. So, I decided to cut myself off completely and start a new life based on the teachings of Christ. Here I've met Christians who believe in God and try to live as brothers. The brass hate them for their faith and decent ways, but these are the best people in the whole camp. They're honest and good. Now they're my brothers in the faith. Yes, I've left the ring of thieves, and for that you can kill me or cut me up if you decide that I've broken your rules. But I'm a changed man now. No one can make me stop believing in Jesus Christ—not you and not the warden."

The thieves listened to Kostya with interest and didn't interrupt. After he finished, they remained silent for a while. Finally, the boss said, "Go on back to your barracks, and we'll talk about you. We'll get back to you later."

Kostya left. For several days afterward, he awaited the decision of his former partners in crime. Taking advantage of the moment, a thief nicknamed "Weasel" latched on to him. Weasel was a weakling with a sneer who mocked the underdog and picked on the defenseless. Now he focused his attentions on Kostya and would trail him shouting, "Look at this saint just walking along! He's joined up with the Christians, but he's not really one! He's just pretending!"

Kostya hid his annoyance, trying not to react to the jeers. But Weasel wouldn't let up, and every time he saw Kostya in the yard or in the mess hall, he'd call out, "Hey, Saint! Let me hit you on the right cheek, and you can turn me your left! Isn't that what your Gospel teaches?" Running up to Kostya, he would smack him in the back with his bony, little fist. In silence, Kostya went on.

One morning as Kostya was on his way back to the barracks after washing up, Weasel ran up saying, "Kostya, wait! I have something important to tell you!" Kostya stopped, though he sensed something was up. Weasel was holding a bundle wrapped up in a rag. As he flipped the rag, it popped open, sending a black glob of motor oil mixed with dirt into Kostya's face.

That was it. Howling, Kostya lunged at Weasel, grabbed him by the collar, and lifted him off his feet. Kostya's free hand was drawn into a tight fist that now reared back, targeting Weasel's head. Kostya yelled out,

"Forgive me, Lord! This is the last time in my life I throw a punch!"

"Don't forgive him, Lord, don't forgive him!" Weasel squeaked, caught in Kostya's iron fist, his arms and legs flailing.

Kostya yelled with great confidence, "The Lord will forgive! This is the last punch in my life! I know He'll forgive me!"

"He won't forgive you! He won't forgive you!" Weasel protested, terrified.

This exchange went back and forth. Suddenly, Kostya burst out laughing at the absurdity of the whole scene. He let go and Weasel collapsed to the ground. Leaping to his feet, he disappeared in a flash. It took Kostya a long time to get the filth from his face and hair. He never saw Weasel again.

A few days later, one from the thieves' ring approached Kostya. "The boss has decided to let you leave us on good terms! It's a shame to lose you—you were a proper thief. But then you went and got religion."

———◆———

After his last term and his release, Kostya started his house repairs, just as he had done in the past. By this time, his relative had died, and the house was abandoned. Kostya got to work on the leaky roof and other projects. His old friends didn't come around to help this time, though, since it didn't look like he'd have booze parties.

For the first time in his life, Kostya got a factory job. Under the thieves' code, it hadn't been acceptable for him to work, but now he decided to earn an honest living. On Sundays, Kostya went to church, and on week nights, he took a Bible and went visiting neighbors, telling them about God. In the first few weeks, he went to all his neighbors and asked forgiveness of those he had wronged. Many mocked him. "When did you become the Baptist Pope? You always used to be such a party animal! What happened to you? Look how you've fallen!" Others respected the changes in his life.

Stepan Petrovich, a close neighbor, couldn't get over losing his drinking buddy. Every time they met on the street, he'd say, "Kostya, Kostya! I've lost you forever! How low you've fallen! You won't even have a drink with a friend! Kostya, how low you've fallen!"

One day, Kostya was outdoors fixing his fence. Recent rains had turned the ruts in the road into gigantic mud puddles. Stepan Petrovich saw Kostya and called out, "Hey, Kostya! You're still working? Take a break! Let's go drink!"

"Hello, Stepan Petrovich! How's your health? How's your wife?" Kostya answered.

"Darya? Alive and well. She's just gotten stingy all of a sudden and won't even bring her husband a drink!"

"And how's your health, Stepan Petrovich?"

"I prop up my health with vodka—that's fine medicine! I'll bet you've already forgotten what vodka tastes like? Hey, Kostya, you've fallen mighty low! You've traded your old friends for this Christian faith." With that, Stepan Petrovich remorsefully hung his head.

"Come in the house, Stepan Petrovich," Kostya invited. "We'll have some tea and chat."

"Your house? Why, so you can get out your Bible and read it at me again? I'm sick of your Bible! Living on this green earth is bad enough, and here you go making it worse—the Bible, God—I don't need 'em! I've got a better idea . . . I'm gonna go get drunk!"

"Hold on, don't run off! You should hear what the Bible says about liquor, 'Look not thou upon the wine when it is red, when it giveth his colour in the cup. . . . At the last it biteth like a serpent, and stingeth like an adder" (Proverbs 23:31-32).

Stepan Petrovich threw up his hands. "Enough, I say! Enough! I've heard this a hundred times already! The neighbors are right when they say you've turned into a Baptist Pope, always spreading religious propaganda! I don't want it, you understand? Hey, Kostya, how low you've fallen! You won't even drink with me!"

Stepan Petrovich headed off toward the liquor store, stepping around the mud puddles and shaking his head. Kostya kept working on the fence. About two hours later Stepan Petrovich staggered back, not as careful around the puddles this time. He slipped, sprawling into a puddle. Cursing and mumbling, he managed to rise to his feet and get back on the path. As he came up alongside Kostya, he stopped, lifted his head, and swore again.

"Stepan Petrovich," Kostya called, "let me help you get home. Our street is a mess!"

The drunk teetered, fiercely trying to keep his balance. His rubber boots were full of muddy water.

"Don't touch me! I'll manage without your help! I don't need a traitor-friend like you!" Stepan Petrovich's voice betrayed his hurt.

At the next rut, he lost his balance again, fell face down in the mud and couldn't get up. Finally, up on all fours, spitting out mud, Stepan Petrovich muttered, "Hey, Kostya, traitor! How low you've fallen!"

Then his hands slipped as he plopped face down in the mud again. Running over, Kostya picked him up and dragged Stepan Petrovich to his house. He removed his soiled boots and jacket, wiped off his face and hands, and laid him on the bed. Then Kostya hung the things out to dry, noticing that the weather had broken. It was a beautiful warm and sunny day, and Stepan Petrovich was snoring contentedly.

Kostya got down on his knees and prayed for this miserable man whom the Devil held tightly in his clutches. Kostya knew that with God nothing is impossible. He recalled his own drunken, godless life and thanked God for miraculously rescuing him. Kostya believed that God is stronger than Satan and would awaken Stepan Petrovich to a new life! Someday Stepan Petrovich would praise the name of the Lord with David, "He inclined unto me, and heard my cry. He brought me up also out of an horrible pit, out of the miry clay, and set my feet upon a rock, and established my goings. And he hath put a new song in my mouth, even praise unto our God" (Psalm 40:1-3).

Another year passed, and at a Sunday worship service, there sat Stepan Petrovich right next to Kostya, singing his heart out: "Then sings my soul, my Savior, God, to Thee, how great Thou art! How great Thou art!"

Stepan Petrovich's wife never did get over her joy. She told everybody in town, "My Stepan is such an angel! He's so affectionate, sincere, and pure. Always sober, and he brings every ruble of his paycheck home. He won't even touch a drop of vodka. He's a real Christian. Every evening he reads his Bible and even teaches me how to live right. He and Kostya are good friends again. I'll probably go to church soon myself. This must be good, if it can turn my husband the drunk into a real man!"

SEVEN

BOOZE WAGON

In the summer of 1992, my wife and I were traveling by train in Russia's Far East from Khabarovsk to Blagoveschensk, the city of my birth and early childhood. We boarded the overnight train and were struck by the stench of alcohol mingled with tobacco smoke. The train car was dirty with garbage everywhere— sardine bones, crumpled newspapers, and empty beer and vodka bottles. Nadia looked at me and asked, "What have we gotten ourselves into?"

"A booze wagon! Well, we'll have to put up with it. By tomorrow afternoon we'll be where we're going."

Only five passengers had boarded with us. Everyone else had gotten on that morning in Vladivostok, and by now most of them were drunk. The light in our car was so dull that everything was veiled in gloom. I borrowed a whisk broom from the conductor, and Nadia swept up the garbage littering our table and floor space.

Drunken shouting and fighting periodically erupted in our car throughout the night. I had not seen anything like it for a long time, and I was awestruck. Not just men but women as well were drinking and swearing. The non-drinking passengers stayed out of the way, silently watching the debauchery swirling around them. We lay down to sleep on our bunks. Outside the window, the countryside was concealed in darkness as the train rolled across the taiga, rivers, and mountains of my childhood.

About midnight, the drunken din mellowed somewhat. If only day would come soon, we would arrive and our friends would meet us, and we could forget this booze wagon. Gradually, we dozed off. Suddenly, I was jerked awake by my wife's scream. I leapt up and saw that some drunk had fallen on top of her from the upper bunk.

"What are you doing?" I grabbed the man by the shoulders.

"Back off, old man!" he yelled, pushing me away, and he let loose with a string of cursing.

"Leave my wife alone!" I said sternly.

But the drunken man was unabashed. "Get out of here, you old goat. This ain't none of your business!" At this moment, two other drunks appeared and forcefully led their buddy away. Nadia lay back down on her bunk, and I stood by her for a while to make sure everything had truly calmed down. Later, I stretched out on my own bunk but no longer felt sleepy.

For a short while, the car was tranquil, but then a fight broke out again at the far end of the car. Next to us, some drunkard opened a window and began throwing out his empty bottles; he was not given any more. Through the open window we could hear the rumble of the fast-moving train and gusts of wind. The night air of the taiga helped to freshen a little of the stench of alcohol. But the icy wind cut right to the bone, and from all directions people started yelling to close the window. Cursing again erupted in the car. I went to ask the conductor to quiet down the drunks, but he was drunk, too. I had no choice but to return to my place and wait for the morning.

Later, the car quieted down. However, I was wide awake. Morning was nearly upon us, though the light had just barely begun filtering into the sky.

I love Russia. I love her people, and for many years, I prayed for a spiritual awakening. But what is happening in my land? Some kind of mass-drunken insanity? What's the cause of this lack of self-control?

These thoughts reminded me of how I had come up against the matter of Russian vodka in Washington, D.C. in 1982 at a reception hosted by President Reagan at the White House. Ten former Soviet citizens who had been forcibly expatriated from the Soviet Union at different times were invited to this meeting. I was among them as a former prisoner who had been sent to Soviet concentration camps for preaching the Gospel and been stripped of Soviet citizenship before being exiled to America.

About an hour before our meeting with the President, we guests were brought to the White House office of one of the President's advisors. One guest urged the President's assistant to provide some Russian vodka to properly commemorate this meeting with a toast. The assistant simply answered, "We don't have vodka in the White House, but we do have champagne."

The guest kept insisting. "It's important for us to drink vodka with the President! This is our Russian tradition, and we must keep it!"

I was sorry to hear this. I realized the solemnity of the upcoming meeting on behalf of prisoners of conscience in Soviet concentration camps and psychiatric wards. I planned to speak of the persecution of the Christians in the Soviet Union, and with this goal in mind, I had come to the White House. At that time, over 150 ministers of the Gospel were languishing in prisons and labor camps for their faith in Christ. My close friend Nikolai Khrapov was dying in prison. He was a preacher, poet, and writer, and for twenty-eight years already a prisoner.

Since I was exiled to America in 1979, I used every opportunity to call Christians all over the world to pray for the persecuted church. I hoped to present this information to the President. How disappointing if a party atmosphere prevailed while the President was making decisions concerning these life-altering questions! I resolved not to participate in such an event, even if it meant that I would miss meeting the President. I approached the President's assistant.

"I'm sorry, but I cannot have any part in this meeting with the President if there is going to be vodka or other liquor on the table. I am a Christian, and I never drink. In keeping with my convictions, I cannot even sit at the same table where alcohol is being consumed. I request that you please inform President Reagan of my deep regret that I will be unable to meet with him."

The assistant immediately left the room. He returned about ten minutes later and said to me, "There will be neither vodka nor any other alcoholic beverages served at this meeting with the President. We shall have fruit juices and mineral water."

"Thank you." I replied.

Soon we were invited into a hall where a large, beautifully prepared table awaited us with a place card for each guest. We sat down, a total of some twenty Russians and Americans. When the door opened, we all rose to greet the President. As he entered the room, President Reagan walked straight up to me, shook my hand, and asked me to say grace before the meal. He then shook hands with each guest and took his place at the table. I requested that everyone stand for prayer while I asked God's blessing on the food and our meeting.

We had been advised that each of us had a limited time to address the President. When my turn came, I told him of the plight of believers in the Soviet Union and of the condition of Christian prisoners. I also answered his questions, since the President was deeply troubled by the persecution of religion. Going into this meeting, I knew that the President wanted to hear directly from those who had personally experienced persecution for their faith in God. Unfortunately, many representatives from official religious groups were reporting that the Soviet Union enjoyed full religious freedom and that no one was being arrested for faith in God. However, I was able to present documented information on the actual current situation.

The President also asked me about Leonid Brezhnev: had I ever met him? I answered that I had never had a personal meeting with Brezhnev and that he, by all indications, tried to keep me as far away as possible in Siberian and Ural concentration camps.

Then the President asked, "What do you think? Does Leonid Brezhnev have any spiritual values? Does he respect the Bible? Does he believe in God?"

"I don't think Brezhnev believes in God," I answered. "He is an atheist and the General Secretary of the Communist Party that is waging a war against faith in God and the church. Concerning how much he values the Bible, the answer is evident from the fact that Soviet officials regularly confiscate Bibles from believers."

The President asked one more question. "In your estimation, what does Brezhnev value the most?"

"As far as I know, Brezhnev highly values Russian vodka!" I answered. The Russian guests all nodded and smiled.

I presented the President with a list of Baptist prisoners, photographs of them and their families, and photographs of demolished church buildings. I also gave him a miniature copy of the Gospel of Mark, like the one I had as a prisoner.

Now on this drunken train, ten years after meeting the President of the United States, I was reminded of our discussion on spiritual values. Reagan had been interested in Brezhnev's relationship with God, but love of vodka had overcome Brezhnev's interest in spiritual values, leaving him in personal depravity. How sad that drunkenness still ensnares millions of people even though much has changed and freedom to preach the Gospel has come to Russia.

As our train chugged on through the Far East, the car finally quieted down. I prayed again for the peoples of my homeland and then turned on my pocket flashlight and began to make notes in my journal.

PART TWO

MY PRISON
CAMP DIARY

Sometimes the reader

Observes it in poetry:

In truth, it is the path of thorns

Of Russian Christians!

(From a poem by the Christian poet Vasily Belichenko)

1966

MAY 19

Moscow, Levortovo Prison—A KGB investigation cell in solitary confinement. Freedom, family, friends, have remained far away. A month ago my youngest daughter Jane took her first step . . .

I have also taken my first step—but into prison!

The cell door slammed . . .

When shall I see my dear children, my darling wife, and my aging mother again? My world has narrowed to four stone walls and a massive metal door. The prison window is painted white and guarded by a simple grille. At home in the Ukraine, it is spring, with an expanse of sky and an expanse of fields, forest, and rivers.

But here is a mute stone grave. My body is in captivity, and there are constant attempts from outside to work on my spirit, to humiliate and break it, and, if it were possible, to buy it.

Through the half-open ventilation window, crisscrossed by the grille, a small piece of rain-swept sky can be seen.

The sky is weeping.

Is it not weeping for us, Christian prisoners, shut up within the walls of an ancient Russian prison?

Somewhere not far away is an open Orthodox church. In our exercise period on Sunday mornings, the muffled sound of the bell can be heard. The faith is still alive in Russia!

I walk up and down the cell. Six paces forward, six paces back. The cell is small for its quota of one or two prisoners.

Thoughts about my dear ones and thoughts about Christ—the Savior of the world. Only He gives freedom of spirit and real happiness! Christ gives the strength to withstand atheism!

I am not alone here. My brothers in the faith are in many neighboring cells. Even within these walls, almighty God is strengthening our faith and inspiring radiant hope in our hearts!

> Christ is unconquerable!
> The faith lives and grows stronger!
> The Messiah is with us!
> Our native Russia needs Him!

On the tablets of my heart, I record the first lines of a poem. There is no pen or pencil or paper. Only the heart's remembrance.

August

The first weeks and months of imprisonment pass slowly by. Despite the very strict isolation of Lefortovo prison, a link between the Christian prisoners is gradually established and functions successfully. I know about almost all the believers who are held here. All are cheerful and steadfast in their trials for the faith. There are now about thirty of us in the prison. Some have already been sentenced. Some have now had meetings with their relatives. My relatives are alive and well; my mother was present at one of the trials. I am told that she was very sad. My darling mother!*

Once again, prison has visited you and I. Since you were 23 years old, your life has been passed in the shadow of prisons and camps: first those of your husband; now those of your son. You have borne many griefs and partings on the thorny path of Russian Christians. Do not be sad, my darling. Christ's victory is eternal! Christ is the Victor over death and hell, and even more over modern unbelief.

---

*Georgi's mother, Lydia Vins, suffered much at the hands of the Communist Soviet government. When she was a young wife, her husband, Peter (Georgi's father) was imprisoned for preaching the Gospel where he was eventually executed. Then in 1970, at age 63, Lydia was arrested one evening as she sat with her grandchildren. Her crime: her faith in Christ and serving Him.

TO MY MOTHER

I hear that you have been grieving,
Mother, so dear to my heart,
Prison once more has intruded
Tearing our family apart.

Throughout your youth: constant journeys
Father in prison, exile,
You walked more closely with Jesus
Facing each test, ev'ry mile.

Life poses difficult problems—
Losses so heavy to bear . . .
Still you are visiting prisons,
But it's your son who is there.

Do not despair, my beloved!
Trust in the victory of Christ!
Our great millennium is glowing
Immortal triumph of Christ.

From ev'ry sorrow, each martyr,
Fruit more abundant will spring:
Strength will increase without measure,
Many new conqu'rors will bring.

Moscow, Lefortovo Prison

The investigation draws to its end. The trial will take place soon. There are two of us in this case: myself and Gennadi Konstantinovich, a faithful servant of the Lord. He is average height, a modest and sincere brother with a great, unshakable faith in God's strength and might.

For what are we being tried? For free faith in Christ?

In fact, it is not we who are on trial, but Christ!

We are merely His twentieth-century disciples, and we are saying and doing nothing new.

We continue to witness to the Gospel about the salvation of man and about eternal life in Christ!

Our interrogators, procurators, and judges have not come very far from those who participated in Christ's trial in the first century. They use the same methods: slander, falsehood, and hatred for God's truth.

There is no question of justice.

Atheism, invested with power, creates tyranny. I prepare for the trial . . .

By now, I have pencil and paper.

My first thought: we are appearing here (before court), not for robbery, not for rioting, not for gold, not for hooliganism.

The trial of Jesus Christ is continuing here today—the trial which was begun in the time of the Roman procurator in Judea—Pontius Pilate.

It is faith in the bright future of humanity that is on trial!

Christ was calm, full of spiritual strength, and confident of the victory of the cause of the Gospel.

His confidence is transmitted even to us.

These first thoughts are lying on the paper in verse. I alter and rewrite it many times, until I arrive at the definitive version.

The hall of the Moscow regional court. On November 30, 1966, in my final address, I recite my poem.

They interrupt me several times. I omit the last couplet.

NOVEMBER

Early in the morning of the second day of the trial, I sketch out a few lines of verse in my cell.

On the first day of the trial, one of the witnesses, a believer from the town of Prokopievsk, answered very well.

The judge asked: Do you know the accused?

The witness: I know them, they are my brothers in the faith.

Judge: Where did you meet them?

Witness: I have never met them before.

Judge: Then why do you say that you know them?

Witness: I know them through the blood of Christ! They are Christians, and that is why they are under arrest.

This testimony deeply moved both myself and my friend.

November 30

Don't be alarmed! Anxiety begone!
Today I must face
A court of ungodly men
To defend the truth!

To defend those persecuted for the truth,
Those who have found life's meaning in Christ,
My own brothers and sisters
Through the blood poured out on the Cross!

Moscow, Lefortovo Prison

A FORMER SOVIET GULAG PRISON CAMP NEAR THE URAL MOUNTAIN RANGE IN RUSSIA NEAR THE TOWN OF PERM

1967

———◆———

FEBRUARY 16

Moscow transit prison. My last meeting with my wife. Where will they send me? I don't know.

FEBRUARY 19

Evening. I am transferred to a transit cell. It is full of men, mostly Muscovites sentenced for hooliganism under the 1966 Decree.

Conversation is noisy. Everyone feels ready for the road. We are all preoccupied by one thing: where will we be taken, and will there be an amnesty? The convoy is supposed to be going to the east.

The guard shouts out the names of the *zeks* (prisoners) through a window in the door and issues each with rations for the journey: bread, sugar, herring. But he does not give everyone the same. According to the amount of bread they receive, the zeks can estimate approximately the duration of their convoy and the district: one loaf of bread lasts two days, which means the convoy is to the Urals; two loaves means Siberia, Tyumen, and beyond. I receive one loaf of bread, thirty grams of sugar, and two herrings.

FEBRUARY 20

We are sent off on the convoy. It is early morning, and cold. A covered truck—a "black raven"—is waiting for us in the prison yard.

We are driven to the sidings of Kursk station and quickly get out of the "raven." Around us are the guards: soldiers with machine guns and convoy dogs. It is the first time I have seen them so close. The dogs become nervous and strain their leashes.

We are taken to an ordinary freight train car—but inside are sleepers made into cells. On the corridor is a metal grid of thick wire and a latticed door.

This is a zek carriage. We are led into it and assigned to cells.

Our carriage is shunted around the sidings for a long time and is finally coupled to one of the passenger trains.

We are setting out from Moscow. Farewell to the capital!

There are fifteen or sixteen men in the sleeper cell. I sleep sitting up, leaning against the wall.

FEBRUARY 22

We spend the night in Perm. We get out of the train. Once more, we are met by dogs, guards, and a black raven. Toward morning we are brought into Perm prison. There is the usual search, and then at five o'clock in the morning, we find ourselves in an overcrowded cell, crammed full of men. They are sleeping everywhere: both on the plank beds and underneath them, and simply in the passageway on the cement floor. We have difficulty in finding a place on the floor.

Reveille is at six o'clock in the morning. The air is terribly stuffy. Tobacco smoke chokes our lungs.

In the cell is an elderly man who will be released in ten days. I ask him to forward a letter to my family at one of a number of addresses once he is free. I put into an envelope several poems I have written in Lefortovo. Subsequently, I will learn that the letter reached my family safely.

FEBRUARY 27

We rejoin the convoy. We are being taken to Solikamsk in the northern Urals.

FEBRUARY 28

From the station, we are taken by truck to the transit prison. There is no railway beyond here. But our way lies farther—to the north. We wait for the convoy for a long time. We are held in a small cell, very cramped and stuffy.

MARCH 14

The convoy, at last, on three trucks. There are three open trucks with an escort and dogs. Before us are 200-250 kilometers of taiga roads. Somewhere here in 1930, my father was driven on foot in a convoy along the roads of the taiga. Perhaps along these very same roads?

We pass through several ancient Russian towns. The last of them is Cherdyn. Toward evening, we are brought into one of the taiga prison camps on the bank of the river Kama. But for us, this camp is only a transit point. Our way lies farther still.

MARCH 21

The convoy has lasted a week. We set off early in the morning. In the evening, we arrive at a timber-felling camp, Chapechanka. Here, winter is still in full force. There is snow in abundance. All around are the backwoods and the taiga. For tens of kilometers, there is not even one village . . . This is the North.

Although it is rather late, I finish a poem for my daughter.

MARCH-APRIL

TO MY DAUGHTER LISA

My dear daughter, my little friend,
Greetings to you from your Daddy, my darling.
In this distant land, I remember
Your tender voice and your songs.

You often sang about the baby sparrows.
The Almighty provides all the food they need . . .
About the tender lilies growing in the meadows—
The Lord illumines them with beauty!

At our meeting, I did not hold back my tears
When I saw you, my own children.
I counted those short minutes as happiness,
As the happiest minutes in the world!

My dear daughter! You know that
For truth and good, for bright hope,
Your father is torn from dear and loving hearts
And dressed in prison clothes!

My dear daughter, my little friend,
Greetings to you from your Daddy, my darling.
In this distant land, I remember
Your tender voice and your songs.

Grow like a lily among its native valleys,
Flourish and sing, my dear daughter.
I believe that God's Almighty Son
Will keep you with His love!

Chapechanka Perm Region

May 17

A LETTER FROM MY MOTHER

My dearest son,

A big hug to you! How is your health? In my thoughts, I've talked to you often and am full of anxiety, but just haven't written. I received your precious letter. It was a comfort for my old years. How often we do not understand elderly people— their frailties and their love. But after they are gone, everything comes to remembrance and grieves us. One way or another, everyone comes into this world in order to walk his path and then depart.

But the main thing is how one walks. The honorable way is difficult. I'm not just talking about financial honesty, but about spiritual integrity, so as to walk straight without bending the soul or seeking only personal advantage. Many have gone down this hard road, but compared to the general masses, they are few. They are admired more after their death, but while alive they are considered 'strange' by people with lower standards.

The spirit and motto of our days is "Take everything you can from life!" But in following this principle people get burned very quickly, and like butterflies scorch their wings in the flame and become groveling and disparaged, spending their remaining years misshapen and ruined.

Your path is hard. I know there are bitter minutes of loneliness when it seems like you're falling under the weight of the cross. Don't faint. Behind the clouds, the sun is shining! You're still young, only 39. Lord willing, you'll survive and even forget these sufferings. You'll just carry the lessons for all of your life. It's good to gain the godly quality of knowing how to be patient and meek even when men attack that which is most precious and noble in your soul. This is one of the most essential things in life. However, I am not talking about the groveling of a slave, because in such a case a person's worthiness and the pursuit of eternal life lose themselves.

I'd like to tell you much about our life with all its afflictions and joys, but not this time. Everything is all right with us. The gardens have bloomed. The days are flying forward, and we're flying with them. What are we taking with us? As it is written, "Their works do follow them" (Revelation 14:13). The years will pass really fast. You will come home, hug everyone again, and once more, the joys of freedom will be yours.

May God be with you! Amidst all misfortunes, may He preserve your heart from bitterness, and may your life be secured in full safety. I constantly pray for you and entrust you to Him, the Guardian of our souls! We will lay our hope on Him, our breath and life are in His hands.

Your mother

I noticed in the camp how the families of prisoners would sometimes break up. You would see how first one man would receive an official divorce from his wife, and then another's wife would write that she was no longer waiting for him and had a new family.

It was hard to watch the increasing suffering of these men.

Yes, it is certainly hard to live without the Lord! However, the examples of faith and steadfastness of the wives of the Christian prisoners called forth wonder and admiration of many other prisoners. Even in their letters, the believers' wives not only did not reproach their husbands with family troubles in connection with their arrests, but, on the contrary, they encouraged them and urged them to be faithful to the Lord until death.

And when the wives of our prisoner brothers came to visit them in the distant northern camps, the whole camp and the entire guard used to talk about it, often with admiration.

In Chapechanka camp in the northern Urals, I spent three months together with two brothers in the faith, sentenced for confessing their belief in Christ.

One of these brothers, Fyodor Vladimirovich Makhovitsky, a pastor of the Leningrad Evangelical Christian Baptist Church, worked until his arrest as a metal-worker in the Kirov factory. The father of seven children, he was sentenced at the end of 1966 to two years in prison camp, and was sent off to the northern Urals.

Immediately, within two weeks of brother Makhovitsky's arrival in the camp, his wife, Klavdia Alexandrovna, arrived from Leningrad for a meeting with him, and brought him a parcel.

This was an unusual sight in the history of this northern camp lost in the midst of the Ural forests. On the whole, it was relatives living near the Urals who came to visit the prisoners.

The other brother, a Circassian by nationality, was Konshaubi Bekirovich Dzangetov, the father of six children. He was sentenced in the autumn of 1966 in the town of Cherkassk in the northern Caucasus to three years in prison camps.

A former Muslim, he had come to faith in Christ at the age of nineteen. He had to endure much and to bear the persecution of his unbelieving relatives.

However, his faith in Christ did not weaken, but became even stronger and firmer. Now he was enduring new persecution, but this time it was from atheists.

I will not forget his joy and his fervent prayer of thanks to the Lord when his wife Tonya came to visit him in the North, undeterred by a distance of several thousand kilometers. His happiness knew no bounds. During brother Konshaubi's meeting with his wife, brother Fyodor Viadimirovich and I remained not far from the meeting barracks, and our dear sister in the Lord, Tonya, waved her hand to us through the window and gave us a friendly smile. She was a true helpmeet to her prisoner husband.

Within three months, we were once more on the prisoners' trail.

The reason for this was our Christian life in the camp. In the barracks where we lived, we three prayed openly by our plank beds. We talked just as openly about God with the people around us. The prisoners, and also the soldiers and officers of the guard, showed great interest and asked us numerous questions—about the reason for our arrest, about our faith, about the Bible, about God. We tried to give thorough Christian answers to all these questions. Some of the prisoners stopped smoking and swearing and even began to pray. All this greatly troubled not only the local camp authorities but also Moscow.

The camp commandant once said among a group of officers, and it was reported to us: "Another six months and half the camp will become Baptists!" Of course, he was greatly exaggerating, but the atheists' degree of alarm was very high.

At the end of June 1967, a special commission from Moscow arrived in our distant taiga camp. In the most categorical way, they forbade us to pray and to talk about God. But we could not submit to these demands.

One of the brothers told the colonel who headed the commission: "We cannot cease to pray and to talk about God. This is our life. And if you have torn us away from our families and from our own homes and brought us to the North so that we should stop praying and believing—it won't happen. Even here we shall pray by our bunks, and we shall serve our God!"

A few days later, on July 6, brother Makhovitsky and I were sent off on a convoy. Brother Dzhangetov was left behind.

We said farewell to our dear Konshaubi, and it was hard to part.

Indeed, "Behold, how good and how pleasant it is for brethren to dwell together in unity," especially in chains! (Psalms133:1).

On the day of our departure, Fyodor Makhovitsky's wife paid him a second visit, together with their seven-year-old son. They were allowed a short, two-hour meeting, and then . . . the convoy.

We were transported in a zek (prisoner) carriage, fifty kilometers along a narrow-gauge railway. In the neighboring carriage, as a passenger, was sister Klavdia with her son Misha.

The locomotive with its two carriages moved slowly: there were trains carrying timber in front. There were frequent stops. At these stops, sister Klavdia and Misha would come to the window of our carriage, and we would talk for a long time, thanks to our kind escort.

This fifty-kilometer journey took a whole day. With the permission of the escort, seven-year-old Misha supplied us several times with tomatoes or white bread.

After this, our way lay along the Kama, the great northern river. We were put into the hold of a motorized barge intended for transporting prisoners; and, accompanied by an escort and police dogs, we set sail. The northern river was beautiful in summer, broad and full. The taiga came right up to the water's edge and was reflected in it. It was a quiet, warm, sunny day. From the open hold of the barge, I breathed in the fragrance of the taiga forest with delight and gazed with stirring emotion at the expanse of river that had opened up and at the freedom that was so near and at the same time so far away . . . We sailed down the river as far as the small northern town of Bondyug, and then we were transferred to an open truck and taken to Solikamsk, where the transit prison was situated.

In the prison, we were put in a cell which had just been treated with insect powder. In contrast to the pure air of the river, infused with the resinous aroma of conifers, here there was a terrible stench of DDT powder hanging in the air. One could not breathe. It was like that until evening.

And then, suddenly, I was summoned to a meeting with. I didn't understand! How did she get there!

It turned out that my wife had gone to meet me in the camp, but while changing trains not far from there, she met sister Klavdia, who told her we were being taken by convoy to Solikamsk. My wife immediately changed direction and arrived in the town even earlier than I, together with sister Klavdia.

They set about searching for us.

GEORGI'S WIFE, NADIA

So now we had a two-how meeting. How joyful I felt at seeing the dear, beloved face of my faithful wife. We prayed in the presence of the guard. And we talked a great, great deal.

The guard turned out to be a good man. He was an Uzbek. After the meeting, when he was conducting me across the prison yard, he asked: "Are you in prison because you are believers?"

"Yes," I replied, "for the faith!"

"Why did you take so few parcels?" he asked. "You should have taken all that your wife brought!"

I thanked him for his kind attitude and his sympathy.

The next day, we were once more on the convoy. The prisoners were led out of the gates of the transit prison. A truck with guards was waiting for us.

Our wives and Misha were standing not far off. They waved their hands when they saw us, and gave us their blessing on our new and unknown journey.

Dear helpmeets of Christian prisoners!

You are always with us. Our prisons, convoys, and camps have passed through your hearts as well. You have mourned over them many times.

Every step of our convicts' journey was accompanied by your prayers. You did everything in your power to lighten our lot.

Esfir Yakovlevna Zakharova, with a baby in arms and carrying a parcel, traveled from the distant Siberian village of Prokopievsk across the whole country to a camp in the northern Caucasus for a meeting with her husband. Her husband, P. F. Zakharov, was from

1966 to 1969 serving his third sentence for confessing his faith in Christ.

One day, having come all this distance, Esfir Yakovlevna spent several hours in tears begging the camp governors to permit a meeting, which they refused her. But the Lord heard her petitions, and she saw her husband. This faithful wife of a Christian prisoner died not long ago.

Lidia Vasilievna, the wife of brother Kryuchkov, regularly traveled from Moscow to see her husband in a distant Siberian camp in Chitinskaya region. At that time, she had eight children.

I do not have the means to describe everything and to list all the wives of our prisoner brothers who supported and strengthened their husbands' spirits.

A hundred years ago, the Russian poet Nekrasov described the heroic deeds of the wives of the Decembrists,* who left their dear ones, their fathers and mothers and, paying no attention to deprivations and difficulties, traveled to their suffering husbands in cold, grim Siberia.

Who will describe the heroism of the wives of Christian prisoners of our brotherhood, who from the time of Voronin and Pavlov (in the 1870s) right up to our times shared partings, sorrows, and wanderings with their husbands for the name of Christ and gave comfort and encouragement to the heralds of the Gospel?

---

*The Decembrists were a group of Russian officers who took part in an unsuccessful liberal uprising against Nicholas I in December 1825.

Who will describe how the wife of Odintsov, Alexandra Stepanovna, made her way in 1938 to her husband in exile in the distant taiga village of Makovskoye in Krasnoyarsk territory? Later, after his martyrdom in prison, she waited for long years until the Lord should take her also to meet Nikolai Vasilievich who was so dear to her heart. What did she think over and experience in all those years? Only the Lord knows.

In 1933, Varvara Ivanovna Ananina, the wife of a well-known spiritual worker in Siberia, came from Siberia for a meeting with her husband in a camp in Madvezhegorsk in Karelia. Subsequently, she also, together with her husband, shared an obscure death in the camps.

Anna Petrovna, the wife of Ivanov-Klyshnikov, served eleven years in the camps, and so did many, many others.

Their heroism in the faith is written in the Book of Life, before the throne of the Almighty. And in His own time, the Lord will bear witness about them before everyone.

In Solikamsk, we were taken to the station in trucks, and then once more into a zek carriage.

The journey was not far—to Kizel, and there I and brother Makhoviasky parted.

JULY 26

I arrived in a timber-felling camp named Anyusha, where I was held until the day of my release.

August 11

A LETTER FROM MY MOTHER

My dear son, you recall how Mary, the mother of Jesus, was told, "yea, a sword shall pierce through thy own soul also" (Luke 2:35). Oh, how well I understand this! I spend each day of your imprisonment together with you: when I take food—God's gift—I sigh for you because you are deprived of what the Creator has given in abundant measure from His generous hand to the just and the unjust. I share your concerns about this new replacement: the anxiety of wondering where they have taken you and why. Where are you now? Whose cruel hands are again wounding your young, but tortured, soul?

At times, I am weak and all but fall on the long, thorny path on which so far it has been my lot to journey. But the mighty hand of the Creator of the Universe and the tender touch of His Spirit brings me peace again and again, "He fashioneth their hearts alike; he considereth all their works" (Psalm 33:15). Firm-

Georgi's mother, Lydia

ness of spirit is found ever and again in Him—the only source of life.

My son, raise your head higher, "Our life has not been given for useless dreams"—you wrote this yourself. When you were born, I wrote in my diary about you, "[Y]et surely my judgment is with the Lord, and my work with my God" (Isaiah 49:4).

My earthly life has run its course, as we sing in a hymn, "We have only a brief time left in which to labor before we shall hide far away from grief and abide with Him in glory." May God bless you and preserve your soul, spirit, and body until His coming. "Faithful is he that calleth you, who also will do it." I wish that you may have steadfastness and fortitude in all earthly sorrows. "Be of good courage, and he shall strengthen your heart, all ye that hope in the Lord" (Psalm 31:24).

At home, we are all alive and well through His grace. The children have had a good summer; little Lisa sings for whole days on end, like a little nightingale. Everything in nature takes its course—spring's tenderness, with its fragrance of flowers, has turned to a sultry heat; autumn has already arrived with her gifts—man alone is restless, seeking storms in his soul. I hug you, my dear child.

Your mother

The first six months in Anyusha were especially grim. During the lengthy daily marches from the camp to our place of work constructing the permanent way for a narrow-gauge railway, I meditated a great deal and conversed in my thoughts with God. In the evenings, I transferred my thoughts to paper.

OCTOBER-NOVEMBER

MEDITATIONS OF A PRISONER

From your youth, you stood up for truth,
Singer of good and eternal salvation.
Now here is the end of your labors—
The desolate taiga and the cordoned-off zone.

The crush of convoys and transfers . . .
A cement floor is now the poet's bed.
Instead of air—stench and stuffiness;
The world has shrunk to the walls of a cell.

You affirmed kindness and compassion
And summoned sons of unbelief to the light;
You preached the deathless ideal
And exposed vice and hypocrisy.

Well, how is it now? Have dreams dispersed,
The hopes of youth, and rainbow daydreams?
Convoy dogs, not flowers, surround you,
And biting frosts replace poetry.

But through the howling of the snowstorm
The song of faith and love resounds
in your breast as before,
And a voice says, "Go more boldly
Along the path of faithfulness to the great goal!"

Good and truth will conquer evil,
Darkness will disappear before the sun of the
Resurrection,
Dungeons will collapse, and their steel finery
Will be given to museums as exhibits!

Anyusha Prison Camp

TWO LETTERS FROM MY MOTHER

OCTOBER 4

[H]e knoweth the way that I take. (Job 23:10)

May God give you wisdom to bear your cross in meekness and humility. May He grant you strength to endure all hardships and also renew your physical strength. My visit to your prison camp, together with the joy of seeing you, left a deep imprint on my aging heart. The sight of these young criminals, these fallen sinners, fills my soul with deep pity. I think that He who created man in His own image and likeness suffers even more grief. What a great task it is to appeal to God's image in men who are fallen into this animal state. But I know very well, my dear son, how difficult it is to do this and that's why my heart is in deep sorrow.

It seems as though Christ's voice is heard, saying, "Give them something to eat." I have seen faces, twisted with evil, turned human again—on hearing just one kind word. And now, as you are reckoned among the wicked criminals, who can fathom the depths of your mother's suffering? But He knows the way that I take, and your way also. He says, "My thoughts are not your thoughts." Trusting in these words calms one's soul.

It is a fine thing to remain calm in the midst of sufferings and to carry forth the brilliant ray of hope through all life's storms. And "He heals their sorrows." These are the words of encouragement that I leave you. "Speak ye comfortably [tenderly] to Jerusalem" (Isaiah 40:2). Let this be your feeling and your language. You are still young and have the whole of your life before you. How I would love to see your bright soul shining in your eyes with hope and faith. Oh, my dear child! May God keep you in His powerful hand and your soul in His deep peace.

Warm hugs, your mother

October 25

My dear child,

I had a talk with Nadia after she came back from her visit with you, and I'm in anguish that your health is failing. Do not hide your state of health from me in the future. We shall go on believing that you will soon be released, but if not, we shall echo the words of the three young men, Shadrach, Meshach, and Abednego. As for my own health, do not take it to heart—the Lord will watch over me. For He leads us "by faith, not by sight" (2 Corinthians 5:7).

If you could become physically stronger, I would be greatly comforted. May the heavens preserve you from any harm whatsoever, so that you can be at home among us again. A heavenly angel counts our tears and collects them drop after drop in the cup of suffering. Take care of yourself, and may the Lord look after you. My warm hugs and blessing.

Your mother

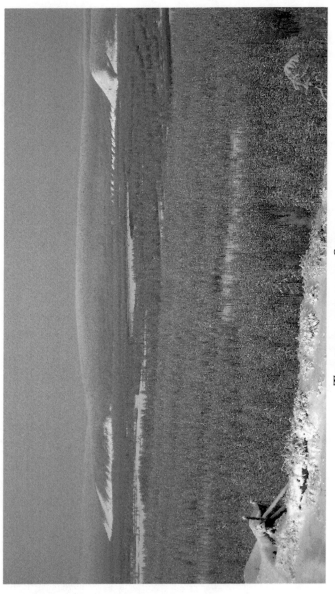

THE TIAGA FOREST IN SIBERIA

1968

JANUARY

In January, 1968, the state of my health worsened abruptly. Sometimes, I thought that perhaps the end had already come. But I wanted to be in the ranks of the warriors for the faith of Christ until my last breath. I begged the Lord to strengthen me.

HOW TO DIE

How to die . . . one must also know this . . .
Not as a crushed, pitiful worm,
Not as a slave, not daring to dare—
But as a fighter against unbelief!

So that as I go along the narrow road
I will give myself to Christ with my whole soul,
And never fraternize in the slightest
With injustice, perfidy, and evil.

Hoisting the sail of radiant faith,
I shall race to my longed-for homeland,
And look into the eyes of Christ,
Who has stretched out His hand to life!

I shall say with a smile to my dear ones:
"My darlings . . . but tears are not needed!
I shall wait in Heaven for you,
The conquerors of death and hell."

In the vivid light of eternal day
Jesus Himself will embrace me,
And no one, my friends, will ever
Take away from me eternal life!

Anyusha Prison Camp

I have not seen my aging mother for a long time. How is she? I have heard that she is under threat of imminent arrest for petitioning for prisoners. If only I could manage to cheer her up. I pray for her . . .

FEBRUARY

The last month of winter. But here it is still a long way to spring. The forest and the camp lie under huge snow-drifts. All the roads have been blocked by a snowstorm.

Soon it will be my mother's birthday—March 30. I write her a poem. But how can I send it to her?

Recently, the link with the outside world has been somewhat hampered, and I cannot send it through the camp post. I wait for an opportunity.

Then, on March 29, I am told that my mother and my elder daughter have come on a visit to me.

Is this not a miracle and God's answer to my prayers and apprehensions?

On March 30, her birthday, we were granted a 24-hour meeting. I read her the poem, and how much to the point it is.

TO MY MOTHER

I would like to embrace you,

To look into your kind eyes,

To say a heart-to-heart word

To intake the dusk as night disperses.

I would like to set your mother's heart

At rest by my return . . .

For the two of us to weep together over Father,

Who bore torture for the faith.

Rest assured that your son has murdered no one,
Has not robbed them, nor brought them harm.
He has loved Russia like a mother,
And wished her good and happiness.

Outside the window, a blizzard has risen,
Snowing up the prison barracks
Around there is only snow and more snow,
And the limitless expanse of taiga.

Winter has blocked all the roads . . .
Freedom appears only in dreams at night.
Only faith, as radiant as before,
Becomes stronger in God with the years!

FEBRUARY

I love you, my earthly homeland, my Russia! I love your austere natural beauty, the boundless expanse of your fields, the quiet of your forests, the calm majestic flow of deep rivers, the reverie of blue lakes. But most of all, I love my people—the soul of Russia. Your grim history, so full of suffering, is close to my heart.

But I rejoice: Christ loves you! He died for you also, for your people, my Russia. For the span of a thousand years, He has sent to your villages and towns His heralds of truth, of good, of salvation and eternal life!

Many have tried to hide from you the life-giving light of Christ's love, or to distort beyond recognition the truth of the Gospel.

They are innumerable: princes and *boyars,** Tsars and nobles, formalistic churchmen and modern atheists.

But who can separate you, my own Russia, from the love of Christ? At all times, you had sons who in the most improbable conditions witnessed of Christ. You need Christ, my dear homeland, especially today. . . . The Lord will never leave you!

MY LOVE AND MY SONG IS RUSSIA

A bleak land of forests and snow,
Garlands of snow tenderly embrace the firs
Between its snow-covered banks the taiga river
Dreams of spring and the April floods.

The white sails of the clouds across the sky
Bear a gift of great snows to the south.
On frosty days, I whisper with tears in my eyes:
"My love and my song is Russia!"

The time will come: the rays of spring
Will melt the snow, and the treetops
in the forest will straighten;
The taiga streams will run
To bow in greeting to the great rivers.

---

*Boyars were a class of independent landowners in early Russian history.

The river banks will turn green,
And the wind will play above the waves,
The meadowlands will be clothed with children.
Like lush, bright flowers.

A flock of cranes descending to a stream
Will cry out in greeting to its native haunts;
On a spring day, I whisper rapturously:
"My love and my song is Russia!"

Accustomed from childhood to bear misfortune,
I have endured partings, waited for meetings.
Protectively, I bore my dream
Of your happiness, my native land.

Believing in a supreme Love,
Which comes to us across the storm of ages,
Today, I repeat again and again
That man's happiness is in Christ alone.

For your happiness, I am ready to give up
My whole life and my young strength;
To say with joy as I die:
"My love and my song is Russia!"

The camp is situated among the majestic forests of the western Urals, on the bank of the small taiga river Anyusha, which has given its name to the camp. It is a beautiful place in winter and summer.

The beauty of nature is overshadowed by the melancholy sight of the camp, blighted by barbed wire, the barking of the convoy dogs, and the black outfits of the prisoners.

All this is so unnatural amid the enchanting natural beauty of the Urals.

The spring nights are poetic. The spring forest murmurs even with light breaths of wind and is echoed by the deep spring river, born in the taiga. The camp zone is asleep, except for the guards. I went out of the barracks and to the voices of spring.

Somewhere far away is my home—the Ukraine; it is so dear to my heart. It is the homeland of my wife and our children, and now it is my home too. The last twenty years of my life are linked in the most intimate way with the dear Ukrainian Evangelical Baptist brotherhood.

Good news from my friends in the Ukraine has arrived in the camp. They are praying and waiting for me.

You hear the noise the springtime forest makes,
How the night bird cries in the distance.
Spring has come! O miracle of miracles!
How all around aspires to breathe and to live!

The air is once again suffused with fragrance,
With sweet-scented conifer needles, grasses, flowers,
With the springtime song of the rivers and streams
And the bright fires of distant stars.

How good it is to commune with the Creator!
What strength He pours into the soul!
And the stars whisper: "You are loved by Christ,
He will abide with you always!"

All sleeps in peace. Only the sentry
Stands on the watch-tower guarding the camp.
But I cannot sleep at the midnight hour;
I am thinking of my beloved Ukraine.

The mighty river Dnieper and the bright Desna,
The shining Carpathian mountains,
Bright spring in flowering gardens
And the expanse of the Black Sea.

The kind hearts of beloved friends
Who raised the banner of faith above the world,
Who keep the faith until the end,
Not bowing down to the perishable idol.

God will lead His people through the storm
To the victory of life over the abyss of death!
The spring choir sings to me of this
And the forest whispers: "Don't back down—believe!"

April

In the summer and autumn of 1968, KGB officials were constant visitors to the camp. I was summoned to conversations lasting many hours. They suggested, cautiously at first, and then quite blatantly, that I should collaborate with them against the church. There were threats and also offers of an early release. But at what a price! The fee for an early release was betrayal of God and His works. At the end of September, I took no food for ten days, demanding that the KGB should leave me in peace.

DECEMBER

TO MY PERSECUTORS

My persecutors, I do not curse you,
And at this hour under the burden of the cross
I pray for you and bless you
With the simple humanity of Christ.

I am pure before you: by word and deeds
I have called you to good and to light.
I have so much wished that your hearts
Would be possessed by the lofty ideal of love.

But rejecting this kind summons
You answered with rabid enmity.
My persecutors, I do not curse you,
But I am saddened by your fate.

The immortal examples of history
Speak of the futility of persecution—

The fires of love and abundant faith
Burn enthusiastically through the whole land!

My persecutors, I do not curse you,
And at this hour under the burden of the cross
I pray for you and bless you
With the simple humanity of Christ.

Anyusha Prison Camp

1969

TO YOUNG CAPTAINS OF THE FAITH

For young captains of the faith,
On their way to Heaven,
I wish for faith without measure
And for courage to strengthen their hearts.

On the way will be winds of persecution,
A deceptive lull, like running aground,
Rocks of doubt underwater,
And the oppressive mist of unbelief.

But for those who are taught by Christ
To subdue the elements by strength of faith,
The sun of victory will shine
Through the gloomiest clouds.

At the sight of the wide sea
Of human tears and sorrows,
Do not desert people languishing in grief
Who have forgotten God!

Captains! Hold the banner higher!
The banner of God's radiant love!
Bring to life on the plains of humanity
The bright flame of the Good News.

For young captains of the faith,
On their way to Heaven,
I wish for faith without measure
And for courage to strengthen their hearts!

Anyusha Prison Camp

The end of my sentence is approaching. Officials try to frighten me with a new sentence. They say that I will not reach home: that they will arrest me again on the way there, and so on.

Many officials come for interrogations.

Before me is freedom.

But freedom for what? For inactivity? Or for new labor in the vast field of the Gospel?

I am not set free alone. My closest friends in the faith are also being released. I write down: freedom is not for idleness.

APRIL

FREEDOM IS NOT FOR IDLENESS

For idleness, we don't desire freedom,
A holy labor waits in virgin soil!
The melting, ringing song of spring is sounding
And harvest fields are rousing from their sleep.

The holy morning of Christ's Resurrection
Fills with abundant strength and thrills our breast!
Once more the message of the Gospel's sounding
Of Him, the One who wakens souls to life.

The persecuted churches meet with gladness!
In many eyes, there glisten tears of joy,
And to our God a gratitude, unending,
Glows with a flaming love in every heart.

My friends, I know how harsh has been the pathway
You passed along, in heavy chains for Christ!
Today you still untremblingly are willing
To walk in far-off places for the Faith.

For idleness, we don't desire freedom!
We have been called the good news to proclaim,
To serve our people still must be our purpose,
To serve our God—our honor and delight!

> The Urals, Anyusha Prison Camp

MAY

RETURN

I stand once more on the family threshold,
I breathe the fragrance of the fields of
home. The hard road is left far behind,
The road of convoys and taiga camps.

I embrace my children who have grown so much,
My darling wife and my dear old mother.
And in my hair, grown gray on convoys,
The snows of Russia gleam as a memory.

And He who is the nearest and dearest of all,
Who is the cornerstone of our life,
Who increases our strength in the battles of the faith,
Watches over us from Heaven with a gentle smile!

> Ukraine

EPILOGUE

After Georgi Vins was released in 1969, he resumed his ministerial work for the Gospel. By 1970, he was sentenced again in a court proceeding in which he did not appear. For three years, he lived in hiding, carrying on his work for the Gospel underground. On March 30, 1974, Georgi was arrested. He was sentenced to five years of prison camp and five years of exile in Siberia. He served the five-year prison term, but when he was to be exiled for five years to Siberia, he was exiled to the United States instead due to a prisoner trade-off with President Jimmy Carter.

Georgi Vins was imprisoned in Soviet prison camps a total of eight years—three years from 1966-1969 covered in Part 2 of this book, plus the additional five years after he was arrested in 1974. You can read more about Georgi's story in his book *The Gospel in Bonds*.

GEORGI VINS, 1979, A DAY AFTER HIS ARRIVAL TO THE US.

GEORGI VINS SIBERIAN MINISTRY

In 1979, Georgi Vins was exiled to America where his family later joined him. Once in America, Georgi started a ministry to assist the persecuted church in his homeland. His eldest daughter, Natasha, actively participated in this ministry alongside her father.

In 1998, Georgi went home to be with the Lord after a short illness with cancer. Natasha carried on her father's work, and in 2007, Natasha married Alexander, a Russian evangelist who had dedicated his life to proclaiming the Gospel of Jesus Christ in Siberia. Now Alexander and Natasha serve the Lord together. Their goal is to continue reaching for Christ the people living in small villages along the Siberian rivers in remote regions of Russia.

These villages are small, from 200 to 700 people, mostly native Tungus and Evenks, as well as some Russians. Rivers are the main "roads" to get to these villages far removed from major thoroughfares and from each other. Siberian Ministry's active outreach takes place during spring when the river thaws and before the water level drops too low to be navigable by mid-June.

Every spring, Alexander and his team of Russian evangelists travel on muddy roads by truck from Bratsk, a major Siberian city, to the first village where they launch their boat to navigate along the N. Tunguska and the Nepa Rivers. They stop at every settlement going door-to- door to share the Gospel with villagers, distributing New Testaments and tracts, showing Gospel films, and holding day camps for teenagers and children.

Conditions are harsh, and Alexander and his team need survival skills to overcome the rough terrain. Over a hundred miles separate the villages scattered in dense Siberian forests along the rivers.

Evangelists sleep in tents by the river where overnight temperatures sometimes drop below freezing. They rely on the Lord's protection from attacks by wild animals at night and unfriendly villagers. Every year's outreach is filled with significant obstacles, but the Lord resolves them one by one in answer to faithful prayers.

Pray for Alexander and his team to speak the mystery of Christ as they ought to speak (Colossians 4:2-4). Pray for the Holy Spirit to soften the hearts of these villagers in the uttermost parts of the earth, in a country where atheism reigned for decades, so that the seed of God's Word might grow. Only our God of miracles can accomplish the impossible to open "the door of faith unto the Gentiles" (Acts 14:27). Please intercede for Alexander and Natasha as they endeavor to fulfill their mission by God's grace.

> Continue in prayer, and watch in the same with thanksgiving; Withal praying also for us, that God would open unto us a door of utterance,

to speak the mystery of Christ, for which I am also in bonds: That I may make it manifest, as I ought to speak. (Colossians 4:2-4)

Alexander and Natasha (Vins) Velichkin

MISSION PHOTOS TAKEN IN SIBERIA

ERBOGACHEN REGION OF SIBERIA

CAMPFIRE WITH SIBERIAN VILLAGE YOUTH

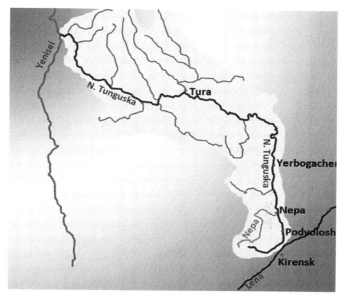

SIBERIA MAP

MISSION BOAT REACHING TOKMA VILLAGE IN SNOWY WINTER

PHOTO CREDITS

Cover photo and page 3: From bigstockphoto.com; used with permission.

Photos on pages 48, 115, 122, 133, 137, 138, and 139 from the private collection of Natasha Vins; used with permission.

Page 60: From bigstockphoto.com; used with permission.

Page 70: From the United States Holocaust Memorial Museum; used with permission; photo #77239.

Page 108: From Alamy Ltd. (alamy.com); used with permission.

Page 130: From Wikipedia; in the public domain.

CHILDREN OF THE STORM

WRITTEN BY NATASHA VINS—

DAUGHTER OF GEORGI VINS

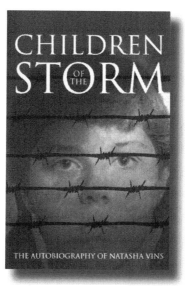

Natasha's father is a leader in the underground church of the Soviet Union. When Georgi Vins is forced to spend time in hiding and in prison, Natasha looks to her beloved grandmother for spiritual guidance, but in her teens Natasha reaches a spiritual crossroads. In a homeland that demands that she embrace communistic ideals and deny the existence of God, will she follow Christ into a life of poverty and hardship, or will she renounce her parents' Christ for the opportunities and open doors which higher education has to offer?

136 Pages | $10.95
Illustrated | Photos
Order through www.lighthousetrails.com

THE GOSPEL IN BONDS

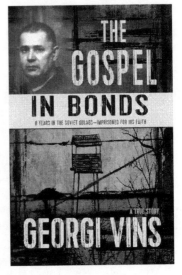

Georgi Vins, a Baptist pastor living in the U.S.S.R., was 37-years-old the first time he was imprisoned for his faith in a Soviet prison camp. He left behind his wife, his children, and his church. Over the course of thirteen years, Pastor Vins spent a total of eight years in the gulags.

But in the pages of this book, you won't read about a man who felt sorry for himself or who wallowed in the misery of his sufferings. Rather, you will hear the true stories of believers whose faith in Jesus Christ took preeminence in their lives and who allowed nothing, not even a Communist government, to take away their faith and their hope.

Threaded through *The Gospel in Bonds* is an intricately woven theme of love for God's Word and faith in the Gospel, even in the midst of severe punishment and deprivation.

212 Pages | $13.95
Photos | Softbound
Available through Lighthouse Trails.

Another Jesus (2nd ed.)
by Roger Oakland, $12.95

A Time of Departing
by Ray Yungen, $14.95

Castles in the Sand (a novel)
by Carolyn A. Greene, $12.95

Color, Communism, and Common Sense
by Manning Johnson, $12.95

Faith Undone
by Roger Oakland, $14.95

For Many Shall Come in My Name by Ray Yungen, $13.95

Foxe's Book of Martyrs
by John Foxe,$14.95, illustrated

How to Protect Your Child From the New Age & Spiritual Deception by Berit Kjos, $14.95

In My Father's House
by Corrie ten Boom, $13.95

Let There Be Light
by Roger Oakland, $13.95

Muddy Waters
by Nanci des Gerlaise, $13.95

Seducers Among Our Children
by Patrick Crough, $14.95

Simple Answers: Understanding the Catholic Faith by Ray Yungen, $12.95

Stories from Indian Wigwams and Northern Campfires
Egerton Ryerson Young, $15.95

Strength for Tough Times
by Maria Kneas, $10.75

The Color of Pain
by Gregory Reid, $10.95

The Good Shepherd Calls
by Roger Oakland, $14.95

The Other Side of the River
by Kevin Reeves, $13.95

Trapped in Hitler's Hell
by Anita Dittman, $13.95,

For a complete listing of all our books, DVDs, and CDs, go to www.lighthousetrails.com, or request a copy of our catalog by writing or e-mailing.

To order additional copies of:
Moscow Express
Send $12.95 per book plus shipping to:
Lighthouse Trails Publishing
P.O. Box 307
Roseburg, Oregon 97470
(U.S. Shipping is $3.95 for 1 book;
$5.25/2-3 books; $10.95/4-20 books)

You may also purchase Lighthouse Trails books directly from www.lighthousetrails.com. For a complete listing of all Lighthouse Trails resources, request a free catalog.

For bulk rates of 10 or more copies (40% off retail), contact Lighthouse Trails Publishing, either by phone, e-mail, or fax. You may also order retail or bulk online at www.lighthousetrails.com, or call our toll-free number:

866-876-3910 (USA/CA)
For international and all other calls:
541-391-7699
Fax: 541-391-7697

Moscow Express, as well as other books by Lighthouse Trails Publishing, can be ordered directly through Lighthouse Trails (www.lighthousetrails.com).

Visit our online store at: www.lighthousetrails.com.

You may visit the author's website at:
www.georgivins.com.

Made in the USA
Columbia, SC
10 February 2023

11569443R00085